Tuning In
To Nature

Also by Philip S. Callahan

Insect Behavior
Insects And How They Function
Insect Evolution
The Magnificent Birds Of Prey
Bird Behavior
Ancient Mysteries, Modern Visions
A Walk In The Sun
Nature's Silent Music
Exploring The Spectrum
Paramagnetism
My Search For Traces of God

Tuning In
To Nature

*Infrared Radiation and the
Insect Communication System*

Philip S. Callahan
Photographs by the Author

Line drawings by James Brogdon

Acres U.S.A.

Tuning In To Nature

Acres U.S.A., Publishers
P.O. Box 91299
Austin, Texas 78709 U.S.A.
(512) 892-4400 • fax (512) 892-4448
info@acresusa.com • www.acresusa.com

Publishers Cataloging-in-Publication

Callahan, Philip S. 1923-
Tuning in to nature : Infrared radiation and the insect communication system. — 2nd edition, revised
Austin, TX, Acres. U.S.A., 2001
p. cm.
Includes bibliographies and index
Note: Originally published: Devin Adair Co., 1975.
ISBN: 0-911311-69-6

1. Infrared radiation — Physiological effect. 2. Insects — Behavior. 3. Animal communication. I. Title

QL496.C24 2001   595.7/01/8 2001

Acknowledgments

Many of the builders of the continuity in science whom I have followed are mentioned in the chapters of this book. Some I should have mentioned may have been overlooked, for the history of science is often distorted. Few know, for instance, of the works of Nikola Tesla, Jagodis Chandra Bose, or Stephen Gray, yet innumerable scientists have built on their vision without ever bothering to honor them. It is an oversight that in my own way I have tried to correct — particularly in reference to Tesla and Bose. It would be impossible for me to thank all of the University and USDA administrators and directors who have contributed with great good will to my life work by aiding me in the never-never land of bureaucracy while not attempting to direct my research, for as each well understands, real science is not directable.

There are a few individuals who have worked at my side and lent their talents directly to this painting of nature. These are Thelma Carlysle, Joan Chapin, Richard Mankin and Felix Lee — my technicians over these many years — and Drs. William Bruce, Alberto Broce, Windell Snow, Abdul R. Chauthani, M. S. Mayer, Charles L. Manghum, and Harold Denmark — seven entomological colleagues — and V. J. Valli, meteorologist. Drs. Kenneth Turner, Ernest Okress, and Professor Robert Bailey, physicist-engineers, have contributed many ideas and so much constructive criticism that I no longer believe I could accomplish a single experiment without their advice. As the young would say of the above names, these are the "beautiful" people of my life to whom I give my heartfelt thanks.

I should also like to thank my many friends at the NASA Goddard Space Center; the Electronic Research Center, University of California; The Engineering Experiment Station, Georgia Institute of Technology; The Willow Run Infrared Radiation Lab, University of Michigan, the Electrical Engineering Department, University of Florida, and the Nikola Tesla Museum, for their useful advice and kind interest in my research.

Most important, I thank my patient family — particularly my wife, Winnie, who throughout the years has edited and typed my manuscripts, and who causes one to ask what love is really all about. Perhaps, to paraphrase Matthew (xx: 12), it is in bearing "the burden and heat of the day." I fear that in my preoccupation with research, I have been both the burden and the heat.

— *Philip S. Callahan*

for winnie

there is a place where the curlew flies,
a place where the salmon leaps
and a river runs by,
where the blue stack mountains cross horizons.

there is a woman whose love is deep,
whose love
crosses the horizons,
and dips like the silver-colored salmon
into the lives of others.

there is a woman who gives like the curlew
to its nesting young,
but asks only that God know
she came to this land
to give to those she loves.

for in giving life, as the curlew
to it's young,
she has greatness above all.

there is a woman whose soul flies,
her name is my love.

A special thank you to a good friend and colleague, Thomas Dykstra, Ph.D., for carrying on my life's work and for his critical review of this new edition.

CONTENTS

Acknowledgments . . . . *v*

Foreword . . . . *xi*

Foreword to the New Edition . . . . *xiii*

Introduction . . . . *xvii*

1. Our Unsensed Environment 1

2. Forgotten Genius 19

3. About Tuned Circuits 41

4. The Fleeting-Floating World 57

5. Tuning In To Moths 67

6. Form and Frequency 87

7. The Wondrous World of Wax 103

8. The Candle Mystery 117

9. The Love Bug Phenomenon 137

10. Tuning In to the Pheromone 153

11. A Blueprint for Insect Control 169

12. My Friend the Nettle 181

13. An Epilogue:
    An Infrared Emission Insect Trap 195

    Glossary 207

    Selected Readings 219

    Author's Papers 225

    Index 233

Foreword

This is a book for modern adventurers and creative thinkers. It's not for those who like mental trips to Dullsville. Dr. Paul Tournier in his book, *The Adventure of Living*, wisely says that "all human enterprises start amid the exciting fever of discovery." He indicates the personal effects it has on us: "When you come into contact with a man who is deeply committed to adventure you become possessed yourself by the demon of adventure."

I found myself, an electrical engineering professor, a complete victim of this spirit while reviewing Dr. Callahan's impressive *Tuning in to Nature*; his adventurous writing style is so captivating that I was unable to lay the manuscript aside until finishing it. It's probably because — in addition to being a first-rate scientific researcher in entomology — he is a philosopher, a romantic, a historian and an adventurer. He calls himself "a generalist."

I further caught myself remembering, as an inquiring teenager, how I thirsted for some great authoritative teacher-scholar to clearly explain — in his own personal way — the mysteries of Nature and the unity of things. It never came then; but now Dr. Callahan's latest book, is *it* for me. One soon grasps the fine teaching quality of the work — a quality dominant in all the better researchers.

Here he shares with his readers in a refreshingly personal way his twenty-year pioneering adventure of how he unraveled the profound mysteries surrounding insect infrared communication and navigation systems. The reader will soon appreciate, as I did, his sensitivity and childlike awe for the highly sophisticated beautiful systems found in God's wonder-filled creation we call Nature. Even to recognize such systems requires sensitivity, a technical breadth, and an artistry for synthesizing and testing new scientific theories which few men possess. Dr. Callahan's clear revelations — some for the first time — of log-periodic antennae found on insects and the factual basis for how they use their antennae to navigate, is scientific sleuthmanship of the highest caliber and significance.

His pioneering research on insect antennae and "learning from nature" — bionics, he calls it — points toward the creation of a new generation of manmade direct solar energy converters. This research is now in its early phase.

From Philip Callahan's interest in the forgotten electrical engineering genius, Nikola Tesla, to his "fleeting floating world" the insect sees, to his elucidation of why a moth flies into a candle flame, to his brief description of the complex research adventure we are now jointly in for "Tuning In To The Sun," I find my colleague's book both informative and thoroughly fascinating. I believe other readers — young people, the general public, and our scientific and engineering colleagues — will both enjoy and learn much from it, as was my first privilege.

But as you read it, watch for that "demon of adventure."

— *Robert L. Bailey*
University of Florida,
Gainesville

Foreword to the New Edition

Tuning in to Nature was written in 1975 as a direct result of an experience I had shortly after World War II ended, when I was still attached to the RAF Coastal Command in northern Ireland.

During July 1945, I took a Jeep from Belleek to Castle Archdale in Fermanagh County, northern Ireland. The RAF Coastal Command had its western Ireland headquarters on Lough Erne not far from our American Radio Range Station near Belleek.

When I picked up a technical report by the RAF on the XAF (10 cm radar) the researcher pointed out that most boat hulls were in sharp focus since 10 cm is a short wavelength in comparison to a boat. Diesel launches under way, however, were "blurred with indistinct edges over the stern." It did not take long to deduce that the XAF radar was "seeing" the diesel exhaust — in short, the radar was *smelling* exhaust by electronics. This rather simple observation led to my irreversible belief that insect spines (sensilla) are indeed real antennae.

It was a few years later, after corresponding with Dr. Ernst Okress of American Standard Corp., that I knew for certain that insect antenna sensilla were dielectric, or plastic-like, antennae. That is the subject of *Tuning in to Nature*. In other words, insects utilize frequencies, not scents, to find their way around in nature.

When radar picks up a ship or aircraft, as we all know, the beam bounces off the aircraft and reflects back to a receiver that plots time and space. The transmitter and receiver are usually a few feet apart so that the return path is separated by a small angle from the "out" path.

In phase conjugation, the opposite is true, as the return is by the same path as the emission path. In other words, it is like an ant trail; the photon "ants" come and go along the same pathway. A conjugate system adds up energy until it is many times stronger than a conventional beam. It is thus the radar *gun* that incinerates an aircraft.

I soon realized from these experiences that the components of a successful trap must be close together in order to obtain enough power to attract insects. That is exactly why small insects work so well, as do the small solid-state, man-made transistors — the components are close together and take advantage of phase conjugation.

Working for thirty years alone, with little help from other scientists, I have now developed a phase-conjugated insect trap (Patent No. 5,424,551 — Frequency Emitter for Control of Insects) that attracts by infrared wavelengths alone. A patent on the more efficient solid-state version, for use on stored grain insects, has recently been filed. It attracted, by infrared frequencies alone, 100% of released male Indian Meal Moths. Indian Meal Moths are said to destroy up to one-fifth of the world's stored grain!

This solid-state trap is based on a knowledge of modern technology — radar. In particular on the concepts of phase conjugation. It is just as importantly based on the ancient knowledge of nature attained by the agriculturally-orientated farming pueblo Indians, in particular by the ancient Anasazi and the 19th-century Hopi Indians. Most of their astute knowledge of how nature works, as it was with myself, was based on observing the behavior of ants and ant communities in the desert. Lastly, it is based on the physics of the scent behavior of the ants in the hill.

None of these approaches are tolerated by modern entomologists. Computer guesswork and arrogance about how God designed things have been substituted for natural observations and for physical experimentation. Low physical energies and the connection of those electromagnetic energies to the atmosphere are rarely if ever considered.

Modern entomology fosters deadly poisons in place of observation of nature, and of experimentation utilizing the science of physics in the control of damaging insects.

The main ingredients of my work have been natural observation, respect for the Ancients, and prayer, all of which are unacceptable as methods of scientific research with our now sacred universities!

Early in my career, I studied pesticides, as did all entomologists. But the findings I released in this book, *Tuning in to Nature*, taught me that attempting to poison insects was at cross purposes to nature and would, in the end, prove futile.

Now, twenty-five years later, worldwide pesticide use is at an all-time high; crops lost to insect damage are also at an all-time high. As I witness our cancer epidemic, I take no joy in having been "right."

A sick plant actually sends forth a beacon, carried in the infrared, attracting insects. It is then the insect's role to dispose of this plant deemed unfit for life by nature. By learning how to "tune in to nature," may you learn to better understand God's beautiful design and come to work *with* nature by enhancing her energies, rather than attempting to overpower and rule over her.

> — *Philip S. Callahan*
> *Albuquerque, New Mexico*
> *October 2000*

Antennae of the male cecropia moth. The family of saturnid moths contains the largest members of night-flying moths. The photograph clearly shows the lateral arms extending from the antenna in pairs. The arms support thousands of sensilla that are arranged in arrays along the arms and detect scent molecules. The sex life of the moth is complicated beyond imagination, and these flying, egg-laying machines seem to exist as if directed by some incomprehensible force; as if some huge impersonal computer were feeding signals from a controlling transmitter into the moth's antenna-detector.

Introduction

In the middle of my preoccupations and secret joys, then — between the ages of ten and thirty years — I maintained and developed my contact with the cosmic "in the solid-state." But already all around, in a half-subordinate way, there was the dawning attraction of the nature of plants and animals; and, underlying everything, one day (toward the end of the period) there came my initiation into the less tangible (but how exciting) grandeur brought to light by the researches of physics. On both sides I saw matter, life, and energy: the three pillars on which my inner vision and happiness rested.

Le Coeur de la Matière, 1950
—Teilhard de Chardin

If one were to take a primary wing feather from the wing of a great horned owl and examine it under a binocular scope, one would be struck by the fact that, unlike the wing feathers of other birds, the leading edge of owl feathers is serrated. A British naval officer, who was also an amateur bird watcher, suggested that this comblike leading edge somehow reduced the noise generated by a flapping wing. The silent flight of owls is a well-known phenomenon. Tests lately conducted under a National Aeronautics and Space Administration contract demonstrated that serrating the tips of rotor blades of helicopters did, indeed, reduce the noise level. This is because serrated edges cause a premature turbulent airflow which breaks up the regular laminar flow responsible for the audible whining sound of rotor blades and wings. The many small vortices caused by the flow over the comblike leading edge smooths the air behind the blade. Observations of natural morphological phenomena often lead to improved, or more efficient, technology. The science of the study of nature for application to modern engineering is called bionics.

For more than twenty years it has been my fascination to work in a field that I like to term "reverse bionics." Man has throughout the ages, by his intellectual and inventive processes, developed systems and workable technologies completely independent of any corroborating or parallel processes in nature. One of the most striking examples of such a system is the complex arrays and antenna *forms* developed and utilized in modern electronics.

From early childhood my primary interest in life has been the study of insects and birds. My attraction was, no doubt, partly based on their beauty of form. Early in 1943, it was my good fortune to be thrown into an intensive study in the U.S. Air Force of the mysteries of electronics. Although I enjoyed my electronic studies, my main interest had always been morphology, and my visual orientation prevented me from recognizing, as Teilhard de Chardin has written, "...the less tangible (but how exciting) grandeur brought to light by the researches of physics." I was blinded to the fact that frequencies also have form, and that form and frequency are as inexorably interrelated as gravity and mass.

Later when I returned to the study of biology, more particularly to the study of the corn earworm moth, *Heliothis zea*, a destructive agriculture pest, the shapes and forms of electronic antennas that I had so diligently struggled to erect on the air fields of Europe and Asia suddenly appeared before me as drawings in the early literature of insect antennae. One might say that from that moment reverse bionics was born in my mind. I recognized that the sensilla (spine) structure, which has evolved over millions of years on insect antennae, resembles to a startling degree — and in miniature — what man had already designed to catch frequencies that he was hurling about the globe in the microwave region of the spectrum.

I decided that perhaps it was possible for a biologist to look at what man has designed and solve some of nature's mysteries, just as one can look at nature and improve technology. It sent me hastily to volumes on antenna engineering and solid-state physics. I was soon humbled by what these remarkable researchers had accomplished without ever bothering to look at nature. I also obtained a certain degree of ego satisfaction in finding out that their *frequency* viewpoint could be as narrow as my *form* viewpoint.

I soon decided that what was needed was not a view from the valley of each specialty, but rather a view from the mountain top where all the specialties could be scanned for an overall perspective. Therein, as in any mountain climb, is both the fascination and the danger. The fascination is in the language and techniques of each specialty, and the danger in the possibility of making horrible mistakes. A generalist does not have a secure position. The handholds up his cliff side are not well known. There are too many languages to learn and one matches wits with specialists far more knowledgeable of the details of each science than himself, and yet it is detail that makes for good science. This is true of all studies, but especially so in the disciplines of morphology, physics, and electrical engineering.

I could never feel secure as a generalist until I learned that the antenna engineer does not really know how an antenna works, any more than the biochemist or microbiologist knows how the mitochondrion works, or a physicist knows what gravity is. If one asks an American antenna engineer how an antenna works, he will say that it "resonates" to the frequency. The same question to a British engineer will elicit the response that the antenna "absorbs" the frequency. A survey of recent French works compels one to believe that the French have coined the best term. The French engineers say that the frequency "sticks" (*se colle*) to the antenna. All of these words reveal the incomprehensibleness of the subject.

The vocabulary of science is filled with words that cross the boundaries of specialties. Basically they mean the same thing in each area of study, but, used within the limits of the special jargon of each specialty, they produce a totally different image in the mind. Thus, if one were to talk about dipoles to a chemist, the chemist would visualize a molecule or atom with a pair of equal but opposite charges (+ and -) separated by a small distance. The same word spoken to an electrical engineer would elicit a discussion of an antenna of two equal horizontal rods, with their slightly separated, adjacent ends connected to the input terminals of a transmitter or receiver. In the mind's eye of a generalist like myself, there appears in the first case, a micro-transmitting or receiving molecular antenna; in the latter case, a macro-transmitting or receiving radio antenna.

In order to understand how these scientific fields are related, my reader must become familiar with a few new words. That is why I have included a glossary in this book. A glossary is like the cast of characters listed in the front of a play program; it introduces us to what is about to happen. For the same reason, this book is autobiographical, for it introduces the reader to how a scientist thinks.

I am not the first scientist, by any means, to weave my life into my work. The Irish field botanist, Robert Lloyd Praeger, begins the first lines of his masterpiece on the natural history and topography of Ireland with the words, "The way that I went was an Irish way." From that sentence he took the title of his book, which, besides being a natural history, is a field guide to the soul of an entire country.

Praeger makes no apology for the fact that his field guide to Ireland is autobiographical in nature. Praeger was a first-rate scientist, and just as his great love for his country was an integral part of his emotional nature, so also was the inquisitive mind that made him a great field botanist.

Like Praeger, the way that I went, and where I am today, both as a scientist and as a human being, has most certainly been an exciting journey. As a researcher, I can no more separate my emotions from my science than from the rest of my life — nor can any scientist.

Shortly after World War I, there developed in the scientific establishment the feeling that a true scientist should not admit to his innermost thoughts. This attitude, although beginning to soften somewhat, is best illustrated by the refusal of almost all scientific journals to allow a researcher to write in the first person. The word "I" implies that a mere human is at work. "I" is not, nor can it ever be, an objective word. It is the pronoun of egotism, and many scientists feel that personal feelings should not be allowed to color the objectivity of scientific writing. This attitude is, of course, inappropriate, for it gives to the "body literature" of science a facade behind which its authors appear to be infallible and not subject to the same stupidities as other professions. It is also the reason that science, which is the study of nature, and thus altogether fascinating, is presented to mankind in such dull guise.

It is unfortunate that more scientists do not write for popular consumption. Perhaps it is the consideration of being thought nonscientific, and thus nonobjective, that prevents most scientists from putting their ideas in popular form. The few scientists who have translated their theories and experimentations into lay language, and have enlivened their writings with their own feelings, have done a commendable job. An elegant example is the delightful little book, *The Dancing Bees*, by Karl von Frisch. Professor von Frisch makes the point in his preface that nature may escape the scientist who uses excessively elaborate apparatus to examine simple natural phenomena. The same fate may befall the scientist who uses excessively elaborate language to describe natural phenomena.

Pierre Simon Laplace, the great French astronomer, and one of the founders of the science of celestial mechanics, presented his theories about the formation and origin of our solar system in a stimulating treatise called *Exposition du Systeme du Monde*, (*An Exposition of the World [Solar] System*). In that treatise, Laplace ignored his own complicated mathematical and analytical work and presented a popular description of his ideas. Even today it is considered a literary masterpiece. Although modern findings have modified his theories, he so stimulated scientific thought throughout the nineteenth century that his work was the basis for innumerable important astronomical discoveries. This is one of the few examples in history of a popular scientific literary effort influencing an entire generation of scientists.

In this tale, the way that I went will be colored not only with my pleasures and successes, but also with my disappointments and failures — as all beset the path of the scientific way. The fact that one utilizes the scientific method — by definition an objective method — does not confer immunity to the passions and fervor leading to wrong conclusions. No scientist pulls a hypothesis or theory out of the clear air. An individual who formulates a new hypothesis does so on the basis of a vast amount of prior research by his predecessors.

Although a hypothesis or theory is an individual and thus a personal manifestation of the scientist's background and teaching, nevertheless, it must have a basis in the substance of the body of knowledge that comprises the science. As Dr. E. R. Laithwaite, an electrical engineer at Imperial College of Science and Technology in London, states:

> *Any scientific theory remains good until the facts which fail to explain it become too numerous to be disregarded. In the light of such new evidence the theory is either discarded or modified. If the weight of evidence in favour of the theory is large, it is unlikely that it contains no truth, and it is probably only one facet of a much wider theory.*

Neil Bohr's hydrogen model of the atom set the stage for the nuclear age, and it has been modified and remodified over the years until it hardly resembles the original model. The importance of the hydrogen model was not that it answered every question, but rather that, like a beacon, it sent other scientists along the right pathway.

There are some scientists who will tell you that science is facts. They are wrong. Science is not facts, it is built on facts. The fact that a moth flies to a candle flame, and burns itself to death, is a fact; but the importance to science of that peculiar suicidal behavior is not the dive into the flame, but rather the question: What does it mean? That is exactly what this book is about — to put the facts of insect behavior and my own experimental data into a meaningful picture of how insects communicate. Once we know how the system works and how it "fits" the insect to the environment, we can utilize that knowledge to devise methods of control less harmful to our own environment than those in present use. By copying nature, we may even be able to tune in to the sun and thus harness its energy directly for our own use.

The sun is the source of all energy, and the sustenance of all organic life, so let us begin this tale of the way that I went with the sun. In doing so, I ask my readers to keep in mind that, despite my computer and laser, my electron microscope, interferometer, and radiation detectors, my way is not the way of a technologist, but rather the way of the naturalist.

— Philip S. Callahan
Gainesville, Florida
March, 1976

Our Unsensed Environment

Chapter 1
Our Unsensed Environment

In the 16th Century the famous Polish astronomer, Nicolaus Copernicus, came up with an idea that at the time seemed quite absurd. He believed that the Earth rotated on its axis. He challenged the prevailing belief that our planet was stationary and that the stars circled the Earth every twenty-four hours. The former belief had been held from the times of the early Greek philosophers. Copernicus went even further, and in 1512 placed the sun at the center of our own solar system. By 1609 the German astronomer, Johannes Kepler, had calculated the paths of the orbiting planets. Kepler also proved that the speed of the planets depended on their distance from the sun, and thus set the stage for Newton and the law of gravitation.

It was not an astronomer, however, but rather the great German philosopher, Immanuel Kant, who gave mankind the first and generally accepted theory of the formation of our solar system. Kant theorized that the solar system developed from an enormous cloud of gas called a nebula. The molecules of this cloud of cool gas were pulled together by gravitational forces until they compressed to a density where the mass became superheated. As the hot gases contracted, the rate of spin increased until the compressed mass threw off rings of gas. The planets formed from the condensations of these orbiting clouds.

Scientists have asked themselves how both planets and the sun could have formed from the condensation of gases in the same nebula. They pretty well agree that it probably had to do with the mass of gas involved in the original condensation. They reason that as the gases condensed, the temperature increased due to its high mass, until it reached 20 million degrees — the temperature at which fusion triggers — and the sun came into being. Because the orbiting clouds that were thrown off had a much lighter mass, they did not reach the critical temperature for the fusion process. Rather than igniting, they contracted into the inert planets.

Our largest planet, Jupiter, has 318 times the mass of Earth, but calculations show that it still does not have enough mass by a factor of 100 times to have formed a second sun in our solar system.

As everyone knows, just as the sun gives off light, infrared radiation, and heat, so does a candle flame. What is the difference between these two energy generators? From a very general view of each phenomenon, not much. Both produce emissions in the form of visible radiation and infrared radiation, and both convert one form of energy to another. Energy is never destroyed, but when it is converted from one form to another, it is lost to us as heat. In the process of conversion, the heat that warms our planet diffuses throughout the universe — irretrievable and persisting forever. Physicists call heat the unavoidable tax on usefulness. The measure of energy's dissipation to a useless form as heat is called *entropy*, and entropy implies that the entire universe is slowly winding down.

Just as the combusting hydrocarbons (wax) of a candle are gradually consumed, so also is the hydrogen fuel of the sun. The sun is an atomic fusion furnace that converts its own mass into energy. Scientists calculate that every second of its life the sun converts 657 million tons of hydrogen into 653 million tons of helium. The 4 million tons of mass that are missing are radiated into space as energy. The Earth receives approximately two-billionths of this radiant energy, yet this small amount is enough to power our entire spaceship Earth. The sun is, indeed, an awesome dynamo.

The insignificance of spaceship Earth is best underlined by considering that each star in our galaxy — and there are more than 100 billion — is another sun, and each is in a different stage of its own atomic life.

Scientists consider that our Earth is 4 to 6 billion years old, and the universe, 10 to 15 billion years old. Even if we are right about the formation of the universe and its age, we will not have solved the riddle of life. What happened 15 billion and one second ago? Only God can answer that question. It is questions such as this that provoke thought and stimulate the research upon which our technology is based.

Both sun and candle are surrounded by a corona (from the Latin for garland or crown). The corona of the sun is the tenuous outer atmosphere of that body. It extends millions of miles from its surface and is composed of highly ionized gases. An ionized gas is a gas in which the atoms, or combined atoms, have gained or lost an electron and are thus charged positively or negatively. Free electrons, since they are negatively charged, are also considered ions. One characteristic of an ionized gas is its ability to conduct electricity. This property of an ionized gas is best seen in an ordinary fluorescent or neon tube. An electric current is sent through the mercury vapor or neon gas which is ionized and then gives off light in the ultraviolet, visible, or invisible infrared region of the electromagnetic spectrum. The corona of the sun also gives off tremendous amounts of UV, visible, and infrared radiation. Such radiations are called electromagnetic because they have both an electric and a magnetic field component.

A basic understanding of the electromagnetic spectrum is central to any understanding of our environment. We all live in a world of radiation, only a small part of which is visible. *Figure 1* shows the electromagnetic spectrum between radio and ultraviolet in terms of wavelengths as measured in micrometers (µm). A micrometer is a thousandth of a milimeter long.

The radio band includes the long wavelengths of broadcast radio and the very short wavelengths of TV and the EHF (extremely high frequency) wavelengths of radar. All frequencies shorter than one meter long (100 centimeters) down to one millimeter long are called microwave frequencies. High-resolution radar and guidance systems operate in this region. From one millimeter down to 0.7 micrometers (red), where human eyes see, is the infrared portion of the spectrum. This almost unexplored region of the spectrum contains 17 octaves of radiation and is the largest region of the electromagnetic spectrum. It is also in the natural "sea" of radiation where we dwell day and night on this

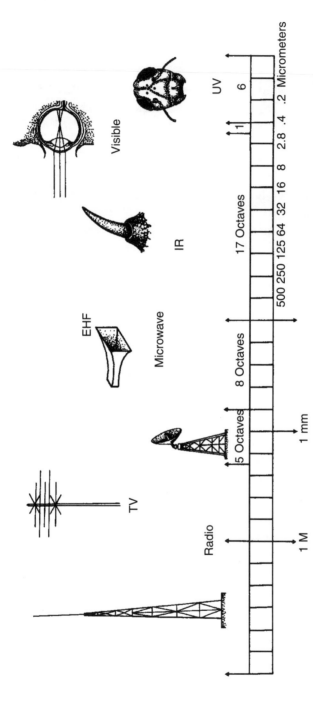

Figure 1. The electromagnetic spectrum stretches from radio wavelengths (*left*) that are yards or miles long through the extremely short waves of ultraviolet (*right*). Past ultraviolet rays on the right are X-rays and high energy beta and gamma rays. Above each region of wavelengths in this spectrum are shown the collectors (antennas) for the region. At radio and TV wavelengths we can use metal bars cut to the proper lengths to match the radio wavelengths. At extremely high frequency (EHF) radio and microwaves, we utilize *dish* and *horn* antennas. The insect utilizes *spines* in the IR region while the human uses a lens, rods and cones. Insects utilize lenses in their compound (multiple lens) eyes to "see" ultraviolet light.

spaceship Earth. Human beings cannot see beyond 0.4 micrometers (violet), but insects see into the ultraviolet to slightly below 0.36 micrometers. Insect spines represent the transition between the long metal bars and horn antennas that collect and guide radio and microwave frequencies, and the short insulative (substances like glass) lenses that collect and guide visible and UV wavelengths. A lens may be thought of as a foreshortened and rounded antenna. In the infrared portion of the spectrum, the study of antenna engineering and the physics of optics overlap and the techniques and mathematics of both must be utilized.

To illustrate how important the electromagnetic spectrum is in our lives and what I mean by an unsensed environment, let me quote directly from a journal I kept on a walking trip I took around the world in 1948. What follows is from that journal, and was written just before I left Japan for China. I had spent the week at a little fishing village on the Izu peninsula. I had asked a group of Japanese fishermen for a ride across the mouth of Tokyo Bay. I like to call that delightful trip my voyage on a yellow junk. The following is what went through my mind on the bright sunny day, so many years ago, before industrial pollution had dangerously changed the radiation environment over Tokyo Bay.

> *The junk slipped silently past O Shima. I took out my binoculars and scanned the coast of the volcanic island, one of the seven islands of Izu, the Izu-Shichito, that lie like a line of hyphens leading into the entrance of Tokyo Bay. O Shima is also called Vries Island, after the great Dutch navigator. I could see the little fishing village of Habuminato, located on a cove that was once a crater lake but which now opens into the sea at the southern tip of the island. Behind the village rose the bare sloping sides of a volcano.*
>
> *Through my field glasses I could see details of the coast that a map could not show. We rounded the eastern edge of the island and pointed our bow northeast toward Tateyama at the tip of Boso peninsula.*
>
> *A fisherman called from the bow, "Hayaku konai ka." (Make haste and come here.) He pointed to the steep cliffs that dropped to the sea on the eastern side of the island. Along the shore rose tall slender columns of rock, and from them the white guano of the sea birds' roosts sparkled in the reflected*

The yellow junk my fishermen friends sailed was a modified sampan junk, pointed at the bow with a triangular jib sail, but truncated at the stern and with the typical square-rigged cloth and bamboo sail.

light of the morning sun. Between the columns of rock and the sandy shore at the base of the cliffs, Japanese children dashed back and forth, throwing themselves into the surf then racing back from the whitecaps that pounded the beach. The old fisherman smiled in pleasure at the sight of the children enjoying themselves along the secluded ocean shore. I asked the fisherman why I never saw a child of Japan crying. "Because they are loved, and when they are young all the affection of the parents and brothers and sisters is showered on them," he replied. It was true, for I never observed a Japanese child alone. They were either with the mother or being carried about, tied in a large silk sukafu (silk scarf) on the shoulders of an older brother or sister.

Unlike the Indian papoose, the Japanese made no provisions for shading the sukafu-wrapped baby from the sun. Many of the children I observed riding happily on the backs of mothers and older sisters flopped about like rag dolls, their heads often hanging with the sky light shining directly in their eyes. Surely the weak eyes of a great portion of the

Japanese population might be attributed to this excessive exposure to ultraviolet radiation during childhood.

The interaction of radiation with biological matter was a subject of extreme interest to me. I had seen Hiroshima within months after the atom bomb was dropped. Hiroshima has emphasized the dangers of high-energy ultraviolet, X-ray, beta, and gamma radiation, but what about the lower energies — the infrared and visible? Visible wavelengths of radiation lie between the low-energy infrared and the higher-energy radiation of ultraviolet and upwards through X-rays and gamma rays. It seemed to me that science was concentrating most of its research energies in the study of biologically destructive radiation. All of the electromagnetic radiation from UV out [right end of Figure 1] are biologically destructive. The sun transmits considerable energy at wavelengths in the infrared spectrum. What role does this type of energy play in the biological scheme of life?

The bow of the junk splashed up and down as it cleared the blue water of Sagami Nada. The warmth of the sun on the smooth wooden deck seemed to accentuate my thoughts on radiation. The electromagnetic spectrum covers over 80 octaves of radiation, but we tend to emphasize mainly the one octave of visible radiation, this being what our human receiver, the eye, detects across the color spectrum. Radiation is not color, nor is it even the radio waves sent out by our man-produced electronic oscillators. These are mainly names for the results that are detected by various types of receivers acting on such waves. All of these wavelengths require different types of receivers for detection. The light receiver, our eye, is not well understood at all. On O Shima was a low-frequency air force radio range transmitting station. The waves from the transmitter passing over our boat could not be detected, for we had no low-frequency receiver. They vibrated in cycles over 3,000 feet long, but the infrared rays warming my body were only micrometer-length vibrations. More than 36 octaves of radiation lay between the two. My body could feel the thermal parameter of the infrared frequencies, but my eyes detected the wavelength of the visible portion of the light rays from the sun. Without a receiving instrument, we were helpless to detect the navigational frequencies or the infrared frequencies *that filled the airwaves. We cannot feel or sense ultraviolet rays, but all the fishermen on this boat wrapped their heads in white scarves to keep from becoming sunburned, for the physical effects of such radiation are obvious in our darkened skin. The layer of ozone gas at 80,000 feet — which absorbs the excessive ultraviolet radiation — saves biological life from the destructive force of such light. All manner of wavelength from the sun is absorbed and reflected by living matter and Earthly objects.*

It was evening when the lights of Tateyama came into view. I could see the village of lights easily because the daylight radiation had diminished. If those village lights had been shining in daylight, I would not have seen them as bright sources because the emission from the light bulbs would have been the same as the background emission of the sun and sky. In radiation studies the background radiation is usually just as important as the transmitted signal — in this case the light bulbs in the village.

We sat inside. The cabin was clean and comfortable — a low-ceiling version of the fisherman's home. We cooked our rice over a charcoal brazier, the hibachi, which occupies the corner of every dwelling whether on ship or shore. The hibachi rested on a square tin which prevented the heated bottom from scorching the deck or surrounding tatami. The fishermen invited me to spend the night on board; so after we docked we remained in the cabin drinking hot sake and talking of America and Japan. At eleven o'clock, we all rolled up in our quilts on the soft tatami floor and were soon fast asleep. The heat from the hibachi kept us warm. We say that heat is infrared radiation. Why? The difference between heat and the radiation from heat is little understood by people who use the term infrared as a synonym for heat. I decided I should learn the real difference in meaning between the two words. I knew that infrared must be thought of as long cycles of waves that fill the sky.

Little did I know when I wrote those lines that the emphasis of my life's work would shift from the very long radio waves of aircraft homing systems that I had worked on in Japan, to the short micrometer waves of infrared.

To really understand electromagnetic radiation, we must understand that all of these spectral energies travel in a straight line. We are concerned here, of course, only with the short communication distances of our own Earth and the moon — not the complexities of Einstein's curved space (relativity). The fact that light travels in a straight line is a well-known, but unique, characteristic of electromagnetic radiation that makes it useful in communication systems. We can observe a ray of light from the side. This quality of light is illustrated in my picture of the soft morning light filtering through the window of St. Paul's Without the Walls in Rome. If the same rays of sunlight that you see in the photograph were traveling through a vacuum, they could not be seen or photographed from the side. A beam of light in a vacuum must meet the eye from dead ahead to be observed. Why? To visualize the answer to that question, think of your own house as a particle of matter. Rays of sunlight that hit a brick wall are reflected and scattered from it in all directions because of the rough, uneven surface — the light cannot penetrate the brick. If the side of your house were smooth like a mirror, the light hitting it would reflect off at the same angle at which it hit the wall. As scientists say, the angle of incidence would equal the angle of reflection (see *Figure 2*).

We may visualize the water vapor in the air as being exactly like the side of your house, only very much smaller molecules representing a micro-miniature collection of walls. If there is no

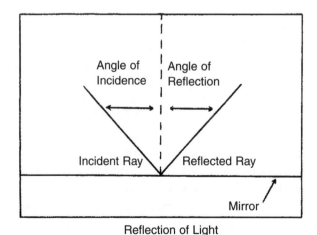

Reflection of Light

Figure 2.

Rays of light passing through glass windows in St. Paul's Without the Walls in Rome. Visible light can be detected from the side as shown here because the visible wavelengths from 0.4 to 0.7 μm long are shorter than the water molecules and particular matter in the air. The light scatters in all directions as it is reflected from the water and dust.

water in the air (a vacuum), there is no collection of little walls for the light to bounce and scatter from, so the light energy cannot be seen from the side. If there are only a few little floating walls, most of the light gets through and only a little is scattered, depending on the wavelength of light and the size of the water molecules.

Since the molecules of gas that we call water vapor have a greater diameter than the wavelength of visible light — as do most dust particles in the air — they reflect and scatter some of the light rays in other directions so that the beam is visible from the side as it travels through the air. Of course, a certain amount of light is also absorbed by the water molecules. If the water vapor becomes very dense, it reaches a point where more light is absorbed and scattered than is transmitted through the vapor. A fog is then formed and we can no longer see through the air.

Whether or not a wavelength will or will not transmit through a solid, liquid, or gas depends on the atomic and molecular make-up of the solid or liquid or gas. Visible radiation will transmit through the solid we call glass, and radio waves will penetrate wood but not metal. We call a transparent hole in a solid or a gas a window. We are, of course, familiar with solid glass windows, but vapor windows are much more important to our spaceship Earth than are the more familiar glass or plastic windows with which we enclose our houses and vehicles.

To understand radiation, we must also know how these transparent vapor windows affect the radiation from the sun. Tremendous masses of infrared radiation from the sun reach the Earth through several holes, or transparent windows, in the water vapor of our atmosphere. The important windows are shown in Figure 3. The largest lie between the wavelengths that are 2 to 5; 7 to 14, and 15 to 30 micrometers long. These are called the 2 to 5 and 7 to 14 and 15 to 30 micrometer windows (see *Figure 3*). I call the infrared radiation that reaches the Earth through these water windows the unsensed environment because we humans have no sensory system that "tunes" to them.

Strangely enough, although it is the largest and most important portion of the spectrum, it is also the most ignored in terms of man hours of research. As an example, in 1965, when I reviewed the literature covering insects and radiation, there were only fourteen published papers in American journals describing the effects of infrared radiation on insects. This almost total neglect of a fascinating portion of the spectrum may be equated with the extreme difficulty of detecting the various infrared wavelengths. A few years later, in the early 1970s, good infrared room temperature detectors were developed. For this reason, the few biological researchers interested in the infrared spectrum at the time were, of necessity, much more theoretical in their approach than were their colleagues who worked with the effects of higher energies on biological organisms.

Another factor in this neglect of infrared studies centered on living organisms was the tremendous impetus given high-energy research by the birth of the atomic age in 1945. High-energy research was, and still is to some extent, the glamorous sphere of research. As such, it attracted the money of research foundations and government agencies. This is an unfortunate circumstance,

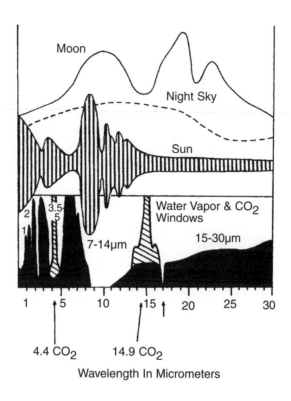

Figure 3. Atmospheric windows in the water vapor of our atmosphere are shown for wavelengths between 1μm and 30μm in the infrared. The solid black represents water vapor. The open spaces between and above the black represent the water-vapor windows. From around 5 to 7μm there is almost total absorption; the sky is opaque in these wavelengths. There are excellent windows, however, between 1 to 2.5μm, 3.5 to 5μm and 7 to 14μm. Past approximately 14μm, there is a partially transparent window out to 30μm. As the black indicates, water vapor in this region absorbs between 20 to 50 percent of the infrared radiation. In other words, the atmosphere here is not completely transparent, but translucent, like ground glass, in the visible region. CO_2 in the atmosphere absorbs frequencies at 4.4μm and 15μm, as shown by the diagonal lines in those regions. Infrared radiation from the sun (vertical lines, center) is composed of numerous narrowband infrared wavelengths. Tremendous amounts reach the Earth through the windows, out to the 15μm region. From 15 to 30μm, the sun's radiation is only partially blocked by the translucent water window in that region. The night sky (dotted line) peaks at around 10μm; it also radiates through the atmospheric windows. The moon (top line) emits tremendous amounts of infrared radiation. These are peaks in the 8 to 14μm, 16 to 20 μm, and 23 to 26μm regions. The moon also reflects visible and infrared wavelengths from the sun. Note the small 17μm micro- or mini-window. The cabbage looper moth sex scent emits infrared radiation in this micro-window, as we shall see in Chapter 10.

for the infrared spectrum is the one portion of the electromagnetic railroad track that is best termed natural radiation.

My research might be compared with that of a physiologist who studies the "whys" and "wherefores" of how a healthy, functioning organism is put together and how it operates in contrast to the medical physiologist who studies the organism when something has gone wrong with the system.

In terms of the overall universe, of course, all radiations are natural because they come from the sun and stars. In terms of our living environment, however, the radiation that is natural to our bodies is the huge sea of visible light and infrared radiation in which we begin, live, and end our lives, and which surrounds us day and night alike. Natural night light is just as important to our bodies and to all living things as is daylight, for as we can see from the spectrum (*Figure 4*) of Earthly radiation, nighttime — as well as daytime — is primarily an infrared environment.

Although we have long been aware of the great amounts of infrared radiation that reach the surface of the Earth from the sun, we have just lately begun to measure the tremendous infrared sources of the night sky. A survey of stars once taken at the California Institute of Technology disclosed more than 22,000

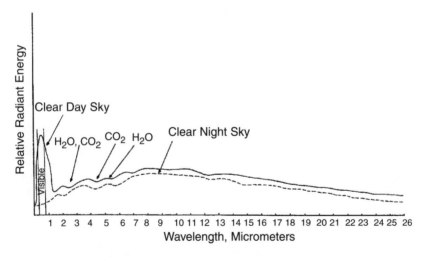

Figure 4. The relative radiant energy during a clear night and daylight of electromagnetic energies between visible and 26 micrometers in the far infrared. Note that in the daytime, most of the radiation from the sun centers in the visible and near-infrared region. At night, the peak sky radiation lies at around 10 micrometers in the 7 to 14 μm infrared atmospheric window.

infrared emitting stars. Of this group over 5,500 are bright sources, and among them over 3,500 radiate infrared light alone and no visible light at all. If man had vision in the infrared portion of the spectrum, he would have put together an entirely different group of star constellations from those we actually see. As Dr. F. J. Low of the University of Arizona stated over twenty years ago, "It is interesting to note that perhaps the most energetic sources in the universe radiate most of their energy at wavelengths (infrared) which fall in the least studied portion of the spectrum, just between the domains of conventional optical and radio astronomy."

Before we examine how the important infrared part of the spectrum interacts between the environment and living things, let us look at the life of the little-known genius who showed us how to "tune to" electromagnetic radiations by getting wavelengths of the energies to march together in harmony. Nikola Tesla was an astonishing personality and should be better understood than he is.

Salisbury Cathedral from the Avon River. This photograph was taken with near-infrared, unsensed by humans, film (0.85μm wavelength) just past the visible portion of the spectrum. There are no films sensitive past the near IR, so one must use sensitive electronic detectors in the far infrared where insects operate. Note that in this portion of the electromagnetic spectrum the green grass and trees, which would ordinarily show up dark, appear whiteish. Near-infrared film such as this can be used to detect physiological changes in plant material brought about by disease or environmental factors.

Forgotten Genius

Chapter 2
Forgotten Genius

While this book was being edited for its first publication, I was invited to Paris to present my work before the 1st International Conference on Biomedical Transducers. There is a museum dedicated to the life and works of Nikola Tesla in Belgrade, Yugoslavia. Since we were in Europe, my wife and I flew to Belgrade and spent three days photographing Tesla's equipment in the museum there and checking on certain statements that are recorded in the American literature concerning his life and works. The footnotes and photographs of this chapter and the next are the results of our journey to Belgrade and also to Smiljan and Gospic, the villages of Tesla's boyhood.[1]

Sitting on the corner shelf of the den in my home in Gainesville, Florida, is an old World War II low-frequency radio receiver. For more than two years, at an outpost radio station on the windswept moorlands of western Ireland, I used a similar receiver to monitor the output of a low-frequency electromagnetic system called a radio range station. That installation guided B-17 Flying Fortresses across the Atlantic to a safe landing in the British Isles. From this type of electronic guidance system came the World War II slang expression, "on the beam." To be "off the beam" meant an almost certain crash landing in the icy cold North Atlantic with, I might add, practically no chance of survival. Needless to say, such a station could not be allowed to malfunction for even a few minutes during any given 24-hour period.

My receiver in its own day was unique. Not only could I monitor the extremely long waves of my own radio range system, but also the shorter, meter-long waves of the military aircraft short-wave point-to-point systems.

If we apply the simple formula where wavelength (the symbol for wavelength is λ) equals the speed of light or current (300,000 kilometers/second) divided by the frequency (F) in kilocycles (kc), we find that from a 300-kilocycle radio range station we have a radio wavelength of:

$$\lambda = \frac{300,000}{F \ kc} = \frac{300,000}{300} = 1,000 \text{ meters}$$

or waves well over half a mile long.

Oftentimes during the long, monotonous hours of night watch I would tune this same receiver to the shorter broadcast wave Radio Berlin and listen to "Lord Ha Ha" promulgating his Nazi illogic. During my "Walter Mitty" imaginings, I might even resonate my receiver to the still shorter meter-long waves to pick up the air talk of a C-47 pilot. It was the invention of the tuned circuit by Nikola Tesla that gave my receiver the ability to tune waves from a meter to a mile in length. I had a ground electronics job, and although at times the nights could be long and the job unglamorous, my hours at night watch were not wasted, nor was my electronics training. As I look back, I realize that fate set me on a path I might not have trod had I never spent those hours on the grounds of Magheramena Castle in Ireland.

On my arrival at the station, I was issued a Thompson submachine gun and cautioned to practice with it. I was told the IRA, who were not enamored with our British allies, were almost certain to attempt to blow up our transmitters. As I later learned from the locals in the village pubs, the political pundits were way off base. Nevertheless, the warning did little for my peace of mind. On at least two occasions, a loud thump-thump on the barred windows of the transmitter room sent me to the floor with speed and agility that I did not know I possessed. Invariably it turned out to be a huge sphinx moth beating against the glass pane. In that rural area of Ireland, there was no electricity, and the window of the transmitter hut, which sat on the plateau of the castle grounds, was visible for miles across the wild foreboding moorlands.

My moth visitors proved more entertaining than deadly, and I passed many a night hour watching them. As Thomas Carlyle said in his poem, "Tragedy of the Night-Moth," a moth is "allured by taper gleaming bright." I was particularly intrigued by the fact that moths were enamored of the large 1500-volt amplifying tubes in the final circuit of the 446 transmitters. I soon discovered that it was the leaky or gaseous tubes that most intrigued my visitors. They went into positive ecstasy if allowed in the vicinity of the huge dual mercury-vapor rectifier tubes in the power supply system.

It was obvious to me, even in those days, that there was something about the pink and blue glow of those tubes that intrigued the moths. I noticed that their antennae were continuously vibrating, and that these huge feather-like structures resembled the three- and six-element folded dipole antennas that in radio jargon we tagged the "plumbers' delight." I had always collected butterflies, but until my Irish days I had not really paid much attention to the night-flying moths.

I bought a classic volume in a Londonderry bookstore. It was written by F. Edward Hulme, the "Holland"[2] of England, and entitled, *Butterflies and Moths of the Countryside*. I read about one of my visitors: the privet hawk moth, *Sphinx ligustri*. Hulme said, "It is allured to its fate by light, coming very readily within the danger-zone under its fascination." Another visitor was *Saturina pavonia*, the emperor moth of the open moorlands. I measured the "arms" of the male antennae and found them to range from less than one millimeter to more than two millimeters in length. I had never heard of millimeter waves and believed, in 1944, that there was no way to generate such extremely short waves. I decided, however, that the moth antennae must indeed be a millimeter-long antenna. Little did I know, at that time, that the feathers of the antennae were only supports, and that the real sensors — little spines called sensilla — were microscopic in size, and lined up on these staggered arms.

It was not until eight years later, in 1952, that as an undergraduate assistant in the insectary at the University of Arkansas, I began to study in detail the sphinx, saturniid, and noctuid antennae under a binocular scope. I realized then that if the insect antennae were in fact an antenna, then the wavelengths must be micrometers long, and not millimeters long. It took another fifteen years of microscopic work before I was able to describe and plot the sensilla of a noctuid antenna — that of the corn earworm moth, *Heliothis zea* (now *Helicoverpa zea*) — in detail. The same work can now be accomplished in fifteen days with a scanning electron microscope. Such is progress.

About the same time that I began my studies in the Air Force — within a month, to be exact — Nikola Tesla died in New York City on January 7, 1943. This little-known genius — he surely ranks with da Vinci, Pasteur, and Einstein — was the father of most of our AC electrical systems. It is unfortunate that his writings have never been read by agricultural scientists. I will quote from his essay (1915), "Wonder World to be Created by Electricity."

> *Books have already been written on the agricultural uses of electricity, but the fact is that hardly anything has been practically done (it still hasn't). The beneficial effects of electricity of high tension have been unmistakably established, and a revolution will be brought about through the extensive adoption of agricultural, electrical apparatus. The safeguarding of forests against fires, the destruction of microbes, insects, and rodents will, in due course, be accomplished by electrical means.*

Nikola Tesla was born July 10, 1856, in Smiljan, Yugoslavia. His father wanted him to become a clergyman, but when Nikola became ill with cholera, his father relented and promised that he could study engineering. Accordingly, he entered the Institute of Technology at Graz, Austria, and graduated in 1877. He next went to the University of Prague, and upon graduation joined a newly formed telephone company in Budapest.[3] In 1881 he conceived the unique idea of a rotating magnetic field (AC generator), which later resulted in our present-day system for generating and distributing AC power. In 1884, Tesla came to New York where, for a short time, he worked at the Edison Laboratory. He founded his own Tesla Arc Light Company in 1885.

His original patent application (Patent No. 381968, May 1, 1898) for the first asynchronous motor was filed October 12, 1887. Over the next four years (1887-1891) he took out forty patents that were the basis for our present polyphase system of AC

Nikola Tesla, holding a gas-filled, phosphor-coated light bulb in his hand. It is lighted by high frequency current from a Tesla coil passing along his body to the bulb. Tesla developed the fluorescent bulb in the 1980s to replace the incandescent (Edison) lamp which he considered inefficient. Time has proved him right. This bulb was made over half a century before commercial phosphor-coated flourescent bulbs became available. Photographs such as this must have contributed to his public image as a magician rather than a brilliant scientist. (Photo courtesy of the Nikola Tesla Museum, Belgrade, Yugoslavia.)

power transmission. By 1890, Tesla had become interested in high-frequency currents, and had built machine generators with frequencies of up to 30 kilocycles. In 1891, he invented the Tesla transformer for the generation of high-tension, high-frequency currents. Strangely enough, this seems to be the invention Tesla is remembered for — in spite of the fact that he, and not Edison, is the father of our entire electrical power system.

Tesla's laboratory in New York caught fire on March 13, 1895. During the year 1896, he built a new laboratory in New York City and plunged into work that led to the concept for, and invention of, the tuned circuit or, as we say today, the resonating circuit.

No scientist or inventor is an island unto himself, although some seem to believe so, and Tesla's work is based on such classics as William Gilbert's *De Magnete*, written in 1600. Gilbert distinguished between magnetic and electric fields and postulated that they operated without the intervention of material particles. By 1800, Count Alessandro Volta had discovered the battery and electrical conduction in metals,[4] and the study of electricity was launched as a science. In 1831, Michael Faraday and Joseph Henry discovered independently the law of induced currents, but it was not until 1864 that a unified theory of electromagnetic radiation was formulated. In a masterful treatise, "On a Dynamical Theory of Electromagnetic Field," the renowned Scottish mathematician, James Clerk Maxwell, showed that electromagnetic phenomena travel through space at a definite rate, as waves, and that the waves move transverse to the direction of propagation. He further demonstrated that the velocity of the waves was the same as that of light, and concluded from this that light and electromagnetic radiation are one and the same. This led to the discovery by Hertz in 1888 of radio waves, which he generated by a spark gap, and picked up with a loop antenna.

By 1878, Sir William Crookes had discovered the cathode ray tube. Experimenting with this tube between 1890 and 1897, J. J. Thomson defined the nature of negatively charged particles, and called them electrons.

An unbiased look at the history of science leads one to conclude that by 1888 everything was known about electromagnetic waves that was necessary to put together a worldwide communication system, except for the principle of the "tuned" or resonant circuit — this in spite of the fact that J. J. Thomson had not yet

The author's wife by what remains of the old Serbian Orthodox Church near the village of Smiljan. Tesla was born in the rectory by the church on July 10, 1956 to the Reverend Milutin and Djourka Tesla. The rectory is no longer in existence. As a boy he rang the bell in this belfry.

Real Gymnasium in Gospic, Yugoslavia where Tesla received his early education. The plaque states that he attended this school from 1866-1870 (10 to 14 years of age). The Real Gymnasium in Europe is equal to our junior high and lower grades of high school. Tesla attended early grammar school in the village of Smiljan where he was born.

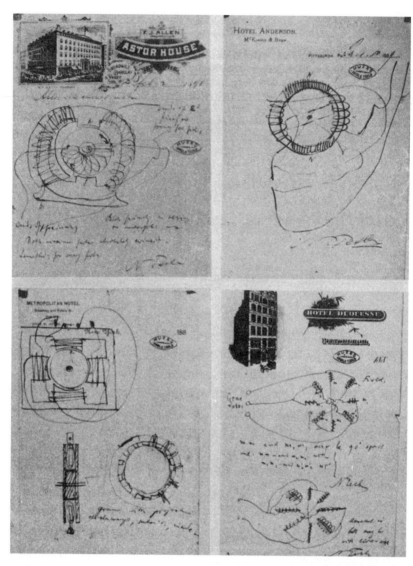

Tesla's early drawings of two- and three-phase motors. These rough sketches started the electrical industrial revolution. They were done quickly on letterhead paper from the hotels where he lived. Tesla spent his working life moving from hotel to hotel in New York. The two designs on the right were drawn at Pittsburgh in 1889, the only year he worked for Westinghouse, and the two on the left, in New York hotels during 1888 and 1890. They seem to refute the legend that Tesla drew neat precise schematics, always less than one inch in diameter (O'Neill, *Prodigal Genius*, 295). These copies show that he did the drawings for his original concepts very roughly as would any scientist in a hurry to get a new idea on paper. Many great men seem to have poor penmanship, probably because they think faster than they can write.

defined the negative electron for which the science of electronics is named. In the next chapter we shall see how a tuned circuit works, and how even a tiny molecule can be a tuned circuit.

Between 1896 and 1914, Tesla presented to the world a series of inventions that are the basis for modern radio and TV. Although he wrote and spoke about a worldwide communication system, his primary objective was to send power around the world without wires. In 1899, he accomplished this feat with a huge 10,000,000-volt electrical oscillator (giant Tesla coil) installed near Colorado Springs in the rolling foothills of the Rockies. His system, which generated lightning bolts of more than 100 feet in length, has not been duplicated to this day.

I am a firm believer in seeing for myself what I write about. I do not know how many of the few American writers who have documented Tesla's life have traveled to his birthplace, but I do know that had they done so, they would probably have obtained a better empathy for him and for his life.

I have always wondered why Tesla built his first powerful transmitting station among the rolling foothills of the Rockies at Colorado Springs in 1899. Colorado Springs was laid out as a model city and railroad center in 1871 by the railroad magnate, General W. J. Palmer. Leonard E. Curtis, of the Colorado Springs Electric Company, admired Tesla and invited him to that town. The fact is, however, that there were other higher-wattage AC power stations more suitable for his experiments than the AC plant at Colorado Springs. The AC plant at Niagara Falls, New York, designed by Tesla, was delivering far more power to Buffalo by 1896, and could certainly have taken the heavy overloads that caused Tesla to burn out the Colorado Springs plant in 1899.

After reaching Gospic and Smiljan, I quickly realized why Tesla picked Colorado Springs for his first experiments.

I spent a good part of my boyhood in Denver 70 miles north of Colorado Springs. As we drove over the wild Velebit mountains of western Yugoslavia, and dropped down into the isolated valley plateau where Smilijan and Gospic are located, I was overcome by the similarity of that mountain region with the 6,000-foot plateau on which Colorado Springs perches — the same rolling hills, set against steep pine-covered mountains as a backdrop, the huge rocks and boulders (Garden of the Gods) piled in ridges along the lower mountains and topping many of the peaks, and the same conspicuous Colorado bird species, the magpie, flying everywhere.

I can well imagine the thoughts that flowed through the mind of Tesla as he gazed out the window of his odd-shaped transmitter building towards the high Rockies. He must have thought to himself, "I am home."

Watts are the product of the potential drop in volts across a circuit when multiplied by the current in amperes. We have no indication of how much power Tesla's system was pulling, but it was sufficient to overload the newly built Colorado Springs Electric Company, and to burn out its entire generating system — an AC system designed entirely by Tesla, and not by Edison.

We must assume, then, that this transmitting station in 1899, was pulling millions of watts. Needless to say, Tesla didn't endear himself to the Colorado power company, but he took his own crew over to the plant and had it operating again in less than a week.

Although Tesla's experiments with man-made lightning were impressive, the real point is that he understood the theory of resonating electromagnetic waves and used the Earth itself as a gigantic tuned circuit for his oscillator. It was he who first discovered that the Earth is charged to an extremely high potential. He used his knowledge of resonance to synchronize his waves to the Earth as a giant conductor. Tesla thought big — so big that he often overwhelmed his contemporaries. Today, in electronics, we utilize mainly tiny tuned and resonant circuits that oscillate at meter- and millimeter-long wavelengths. This does not detract from the fact that Patent No. 649621 (filed September 2, 1897, and called "Apparatus for Transmission of Electrical Energy") was the first tuned circuit. Tesla's patents are dated at least two years before Marconi was even off to a good start.

Before we look at what a tuned circuit really is, let us finish with the life of this strange genius, Tesla. He emerges from O'Neill's biography[5] as a kind, overgenerous, well-dressed Victorian recluse with quite a few phobias, one of which was germs — he never shook hands for fear of transmitting them. Another was women — he never married. Tesla was what has been called a "lone wolf."[6] Had he married and united his life to a bright Victorian wife who could have handled his finances and personal matters — as Edison did — he might have been recognized as the genius he was. As with da Vinci, it will probably be several hundred years before Tesla's real worth is understood.

Tesla insisted until his death that he was materialistic, rationalistic, and agnostic. He went to school during the age of reason when most scientists — with the exception of a few such as Sir William Crookes — believed in materialistic, natural philosophy. Everything was based on the newly discovered experimental method, and there was no such thing as a spiritual universe.

Fortunately there is a swing back in the other direction, and more and more scientists are adopting a philosophy similar to that of the famous paleontologist, Teilhard de Chardin, who was first a mystic, then a scientist — just as Sir William Crookes was first a scientist, then a mystic. Scientists have finally condescended to look at such phenomena as ESP (extrasensory perception). However, before he died, Tesla said, "The day science begins to study nonphysical phenomena, it will make more progress in one decade than in the previous centuries of existence." This is hardly the statement of a believing rationalist.

In 1898, Tesla built and demonstrated in Madison Square Garden, New York, the first completely radio-controlled moving vehicle: a boat (Patent No. 613809, filed July 1, 1898). Remote control weaponry began with Tesla, and its misuse in war was a constant worry to him. Tesla was guiding his remote radio-controlled boat around a pond in Madison Square Garden more than four years before Marconi built his transmitters on the Salisbury Plain in England. In 1895, in Bologna, Italy, Marconi transmitted signals over a distance of one kilometer, but his system was not, however, nearly as sophisticated as that of Tesla.

Tesla experimented with the gas discharge tubes of Crookes, and knew about the ultraviolet emission that he called "black light." He is thus the father of the entomologist's black light bulb — a bulb that gives off near-ultraviolet light and is used to attract and trap night-flying insects. He also described other strong rays that come from some of his tubes. Although Roentgen discovered X-rays accidentally, and named them, Tesla, during the same period, was taking pictures with X-rays from forty feet while Roentgen was still struggling with his X-ray radiation over distances of inches. There is considerable evidence that Tesla knew all about these rays and was experimenting with black light, as well as X-rays, which he called "long special radiations." He described them as early as 1892. At that time he had already produced "shadow proofs" — X-ray pictures on plates in metal containers. Shortly after, his laboratory was destroyed and his records lost. Tesla did not try to share credit for Roentgen's discovery of X-rays in December 1895, but had he been of a less generous nature, he certainly would have done so.

Everyone should be interested in Tesla, for our whole technological age is based on his discoveries. The printing of this book depends on his AC generator and motor.

Entomologists should be particularly interested in Tesla, if for no other reason than that he invented the black light. Interestingly enough, at age nine he also invented the insect flight mill. Today, entomologists study insect flight with a similar flight mill. Tesla called it his 16-bug power engine. He crossed two thin sticks and glued sixteen June bugs — four per arm — to the cross arms. He balanced the cross on a thin wooden spindle, to which he attached a small, pea-sized pulley. Using thread as a drive belt to a larger pulley, he calculated the torque and turning power of his bug machine as the beetles flew around and around at high speed. This is, quite obviously, the principle of the entomologist's flight mill.

George Westinghouse, also an inventor, was one of Tesla's good friends. In 1888, he paid $1,000,000[7]-plus a dollar per horsepower for Tesla's 3-phase AC generator. Edison's DC system could not be transmitted over great distances, and it was Westinghouse who took Tesla's AC 3-phase generator system and built it into our present power system.

Later, when George Westinghouse was backed against a financial wall during the period of the money "robber barons," he went to Tesla and asked to be relieved of the dollar-per-horsepower agreement. As an insight into the character of Tesla, we need only note that he must have valued friendship more than money, for he tore up his contract. If he had held Westinghouse to the contract, he would have remained a millionaire for the rest of his life.

Tesla financed his own experiments. He was extremely generous to his help, and his equipment was gigantic; consequently, his experiments were very expensive. During one year, he worked for Westinghouse but, as is usual, the management tried to direct his thinking, so he left in disgust and would never again work for anyone else. Tesla was an incompetent businessman, and he gradually ran out of funds for research. He never sued to recover royalties from the inventions he had perfected, and that industry had utilized without ever returning a penny to the scientist-inventor. He died a lonely, neglected man at the age of 86, on January 7, 1943, in a room at the Hotel New Yorker where he spent the last ten years of his life.

Although, during the height of his career, Tesla received fourteen honorary degrees, only two came from American universities — Yale and Columbia. Strangely enough, he has been almost completely eliminated from college textbooks on physics and the history of science. *Physics for Biologists and Chemists* (Hughes and Latham, 1968) makes no mention of his work; nor do many college level books.

According to John O'Neill, when Tesla died in 1943 his papers were taken — confiscated might be a better term — by the FBI, and sealed by the Custodian of Alien Property, although Tesla had been an American citizen for many years.[8]

At the turn of the century, Tesla was recognized by his own fellow scientists. It is known that in 1912 he refused the Nobel Prize — the only man in history to do so. Some say it was because he believed he should have received it in 1909, when Marconi did.[9] Tesla was a peculiar figure, and we will probably never know exactly why he turned it down. It is somewhat of a paradox, however, that it was awarded instead to the Swedish engineer, Gustav Dalen, for inventing a regulator for gas lights. Gas lighting was already being replaced by Tesla's AC power. Somehow, a Nobel Prize for a gas-light regulator does not seem to be an overly elegant conception. Dalen also invented the milking machine. As an agriculturist, I believe the prize could just as well have been awarded for that hand-saving device. For those among us researchers overly awed by Nobel Prizes, it soothes our pride to know that even that august body sometimes touches Earth with such mundane things as gas-light regulators.

I have before me more than ninety of Tesla's patents. Anyone reading them carefully, and checking the dates against those of the great discoveries in electronics, must conclude that most of the significant research in that field was taking place between 1880 and 1900. Hertz demonstrated electromagnetic waves in 1887, and Tesla patented his two- and three-phase alternators and induction motors the same year. In 1897, J. J. Thomson discovered the electron. He received the Nobel Prize for his work with the electron in 1906. Tesla and Thomson both worked with gas discharge tubes, and their writings indicate that they respected, and knew of, each other's research. Tesla came up with his tuned circuits in 1897.

We will never know for what Tesla was going to receive the Nobel Prize — probably the AC motor and not the tuned circuit. At the present time, few people seem to realize the significance of his discovery of the resonant circuit, although it put all of the electron soldiers of Thomson in marching order. Either discovery would certainly be worthy of the honor — far more so than a gas lamp regulator. A good historian, however, must look at such things in the light of the age in which they happened. He may observe without bias from afar, but he must still possess the ability to transport himself back to another age. He must place himself in the shoes of the people who lived in the period being studied. The Nobel Prize is given not only for science, but also for service to humanity. In all fairness to Dalen, there is no telling how many Victorian lives may have been saved from asphyxiation by his gas regulator. Gas was, after all, the main source of illumination at the turn of the century.

Why has the name of Tesla been so neglected by present-day science? In my opinion there are three main reasons: his character, the Victorian period he worked in, and, last but not least, what is known in the vernacular of our times as "effete snobbism" on the part of today's scientists.

The *Encyclopedia Britannica* has several pages on Edison, but only a single paragraph about Tesla. It recognizes his AC motor, but says nothing about the tuned circuit, or about his other great inventions. Edison was a trial-and-error experimenter, but Tesla was a scientist. He used mathematics to arrive at many of the concepts that he turned into inventions. Both men were geniuses in their own way, but Edison was not the eccentric that Tesla was. Tesla had visions. At school he was almost expelled for cheating before it was discovered that he did not cheat; he worked his calculus problems in his head. He was one of the few men in history who combined the brain of a calculator with the imagination of a scientist. A "genetic superman" is O'Neill's term. People with photographic memories seldom have the imagination to become great scientists, and even Einstein required a blackboard. Tesla did his engineering drawings in minute detail, without ever measuring a line.[10] When his workmen machined parts from his drawings, they all fit perfectly.

Edison worked well with other people and formed a research group; Tesla would not. Tesla never published in a scientific journal, and from this standpoint his photographic/calculator mind was a drawback, because very few of the subtle mathematical calculations of his designs exist on paper. Since he did not publish in journals (proving the validity of "publish or perish"), he is considered today an engineer and an inventor, but not a scientist, by American university groups. After all, what dean or administrator counts patents. Tesla had many close friends, but because he was essentially a recluse, and a mystic, the scientists — even those of his own age — were reluctant to associate with him. They did, however, as I must reemphasize, recognize his genius.

The Victorian Age was an era of rationalism in science, and although Tesla protested time and again that he was a factual scientist, in the very next breath he talked about his visions. He said the concept of the AC motor came to him in a vision while he was gazing at the sun in Budapest. How does a Nobel committee measure a vision? Insight is probably a more acceptable term than vision to most scientists. One cannot explain insight any more than one can explain love. Both are mystical experiences, and the Victorian age of reason denied their existence. The word mystic comes from the word mystery, and the mystery of science is that creation is stranger today — with its electrons and quarks, its quasars and masers — than it ever was in past ages.

Certainly, turning down a Nobel Prize did not enhance the image of Tesla. It is true that he was aloof, but only in his personal habits — not in his research. Tesla's laboratory was open to all, and he shared his ideas with others to the end that he was constantly taken advantage of, and his ideas stolen. His science was at once practical and visionary, idealistic, and totally unselfish. What matters is not that a scientist is aloof in his personal tastes, but rather that he not be an intellectual snob. Even worse is the danger that an entire scientific organization may evolve a form of snobbism that excludes all but the chosen elite. Tesla could never tolerate such a group, nor should any thinking scientist, and yet that is exactly what is happening in many areas of science today: the biggest enemies of science are scientists — not a lack of research money. The history of science provides many examples of the intimidation of researchers by the elite. One of the best, or perhaps I should say the most horrible, is concerned with the discovery of radio waves. It is well documented in the minutes of the Royal Society of London for the Advancement of Science that as early as 1879 Professor David Hughes, the inventor of the microphone, observed invisible electric waves, which he detected with his sensitive microphone contacts.

Between 1879 and 1886, Hughes experimented extensively with his waves and demonstrated aerial transmissions over great distances. He was invited to demonstrate the newly discovered phenomenon before the Royal Society — an invitation that, unfortunately, he accepted. After a three-hour demonstration, the Honourable Secretary of the Royal Society, a Professor Stokes, decided that there was no evidence for the long, invisible electromagnetic waves, and that the phenomenon was merely an induction effect. Poor Professor Hughes was so intimidated by this supposed authority that he refused to publish his results, despite urging by his friends. This left the entire field open to Hertz and Marconi. Alas, today we call an electromagnetic wave cycle a "Hertz" and not a "Hughes." To add insult to injury, Professor Stokes later paid tribute to Hertz and Marconi for their great discovery. Let that be a lesson to timid minds overly impressed by elite leaders in certain research fields who may well not be leading at all but, rather, suppressing.

Tesla may have been ignored and played with by the leaders of his day — the effete snobs of industry and politics — but he certainly was not ignored by his scientific colleagues; fourteen honorary degrees attest to that. Whatever the snobbery of the Victorian Age, it seldom (with a few exceptions, as in Hughes's case) reached into the scientific community where there was a free exchange of exciting new concepts. Tesla's essay indicates a lively exchange between the scientists, young and old, of his day. There was no such thing as an unsigned, anonymous peer review of a research paper such as we see today. Every man accepted responsibility for his own theories and experiments and fought the good fight to get his thoughts across without fear of anonymous peer censorship from small minds. What mattered was not that a theory was right or wrong, but that it caused other scientists to question and rethink other, more traditional ideas. Science cannot afford to be traditional. Science does not progress by traditional beliefs, but rather by radical new ideas of single, imaginative minds. Who would deny that Darwin and Einstein were two of our greatest scientific radicals? No committee has ever come up with a single revolutionary new concept. Only individuals have concepts. A scientist is an individual who conceptualizes new theories or techniques because he loves what he does — never because some dean or director decides what he should or should not be doing. There can be directed technology, but never directed science.

In 1946, while working as a civilian for the Far East Pacific Air Force, I supervised and helped design the installation of the low-frequency radio range on O Shima Island in Tokyo Bay. We built it from old Japanese equipment, and it pulled over 100,000 watts at 100 kc. The station put out a beam across the water for more than 500 miles. At 100 kc, the waves were 3,000 meters long. To tune the transmission lines to resonance, in order to maximize the feed to the huge steel towers, we used a tuned circuit with condenser plates over three feet in diameter. As far as I know, at that time it was the most powerful very-low-frequency radio station in the world — a "Tesla-type" station. Now I work in the infrared with waves only micrometers long, and with molecular "tuned circuits" that put out oscillation energies of less than 10^{-14} to 10^{-17} watts. Like Tesla, I have gone from one extreme to the other.

As I look back to my low-frequency radio days, and the mercury vapor tubes in the old 446 transmitter, I realize that the molecules in the air around the tube were being stimulated to oscillate by the shortwave radiations from the tube. I know now that, surrounding the outside of the tube emitting visible, IR, and black light (UV) from within its glass envelope, there is an aurora of invisible infrared emissions of many, many wavelengths, depending on what molecules are in the air. There exists a huge population of free-floating molecular emissions, many with harmonics, that confuse and bewilder those insect night-flyers. This complex of stimulated infrared frequencies surrounding gas discharge tubes is more mysterious than the visible and UV light reaching the eye of the moth. The same may be said for the aurora of the IR frequencies rising from a cotton or corn field, or encircling the mammalian body. Over and around such fields and bodies are vapors of scent molecules stimulated to oscillate as little transmitting "tuned circuits" by the energies of sun and night-sky light.

Those who knew him say that Nikola Tesla had a sense of humor. He built a huge Tesla transformer above and below his doorway. When a person he did not like came through the door, he would throw a switch and their hair would stand straight up in the air from the charge. Needless to say, the person seldom returned.

In 1956, as a young newly graduated Ph.D., I attended the 1956 meeting of the Entomological Society of America at the Hotel New Yorker in Manhattan. My paper on light and the corn earworm was the very first paper at 8:00 in the morning. I am not sure, but I believe that at that time the New Yorker was still on Edison's old DC 210 power system. At any rate, when the chairman plugged in the projector, it went up in smoke. It was obvious that it would be some time before a new projector could be found. The chairman asked me if I would go on so as not to delay the meeting. There I stood, an egotistical jackass with a new Ph.D. and what I thought was the most important piece of research on the corn earworm moth in existence. I was at first upset, then angry, and finally calm. I suddenly decided that since I had done the work, I should know enough about it to give the paper without the slides. I must have done a fair job because Dr. Clyde Smith, Chairman of the Entomology Department at North Carolina State University, walked up when I was finished to offer me a job.

Only thirteen years before, 86-year-old Nikola Tesla had died in a room just above where I spoke. Today, I like to think that the ghost of Nikola Tesla was in that room laughing as he pulled the switch on my projector — and to believe that what he was really doing was seeing if the young egotist had the guts to keep working with his marvelous tuned circuits. I like to believe that he wanted me to keep going and not give up, regardless of what others thought, or did, or said — and to think that he not only sent one of his long undulating "lightning bolt" sine waves into the projector, but also into my brain, so that I would never forget that form and frequency go together like ham and eggs. Maybe his ghost upstairs was saying to me that life will always be a mystery no matter what we humans discover. I know I believe that now. The more I learn, the less I know, and life will always be a journey to new moons. You see, I am a mystic too.

Footnotes

[1]Our two weeks in the countryside of Tesla's youth proved to be one of the most fascinating journeys of our lives. Nikola Tesla is not a "forgotten genius" in Yugoslavia, for everyone we spoke to knew about his life and discoveries. The good people of Belgrade, Gospic and the crossroad village of Smilian went out of their way to see that we obtained everything we needed and every photograph we wished.

[2]The recognized American moth and butterfly entomologist, W. J. Holland.

[3]There is no indication that Tesla graduated from the university, as his biographer, John J. O'Neill, maintains *(Prodigal Genius*, p. 45). Tesla probably had no degree from a university other than honorary.

[4]Stephen Gray discovered conduction in 1733 in pack cord (string), a non-metal material, so is the real father of electricity. It would take a book to cover the experiments of this little known English genius.

[5]*Prodigal Genius* by John J. O'Neill, Ives Washburn, Inc., 1944.

[6]Tesla was very definitely a bird lover. As a boy, he kept a pet hawk, and in later years when asked what his hobby was, he replied, "caring for sick birds." He invited city pigeons into his hotel room and fed them.

[7]Cold business reports place this figure nearer $200,000 paid, not to Tesla, but to the Tesla Electric Co. of which he owned one-third interest. Thus, his personal share was really a little over $65,000 *(Tribute to Nikola Tesla*, p. 366, Nikola Tesla Museum, Belgrade).

[8]In accordance with his will, the entire works of Nikola Tesla, including his original notebooks, have been deposited in the Nikola Tesla Museum in Belgrade, Yugoslavia. Whether or not the notebooks from his hotel room (sealed during World War II) were eventually sent to the Museum, is unknown to this author.

[9]Marconi is definitely not the discoverer of the tuned circuit, which is what radio is based on. (See United States Reports, Vol. 320: Cases Adjudged in the Supreme Court at Oct. Term, 1942, and Oct. Term, 1943: MARCONI WIRELESS CO. V. U.S. This report contains the decision in which the Marconi "four-tuned circuit" was declared invalid on the basis of prior disclosure by Tesla and Stone (pp. 1-80).

It is clear, from this decision, that Tesla's tuned-circuit discovery in 1897 was kept tied up in the courts from the turn of the century until 1943-the year of his death. No wonder he died poor.

[10]This may be another legend (see photograph p. 28).

About Tuned Circuits

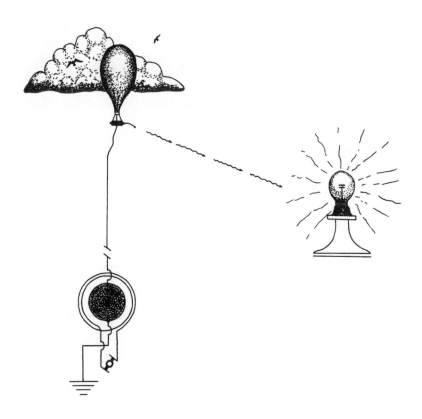

Chapter 3

About Tuned Circuits

Why is the invention of the tuned circuit by this fascinating man, Nikola Tesla, so important? Let us take a quick look at what a tuned circuit really is. Resonant waves have been known ever since man invented the first stringed musical instrument. Most people seem to understand how sound resonance works, but many apparently draw a complete blank when the subject of electrical resonance is approached. From this standpoint, electrical resonance seems to have suffered the same fate as Tesla himself — obscurity.

A wave, as you may know, is made up of a series of crests and troughs; this holds true for liquid waves, sound waves, and electromagnetic waves — regardless of how long or short they are. If by some means, mechanical or otherwise, waves are put in "phase," then the crest of one meets the crest of the other, and waves march in unison and thus add together. If they are 180 degrees out of phase — so that waves and troughs are opposite each other — then they cancel out, and the result is no wave or zero. In wave terminology this is called constructive (addition) or destructive (cancellation) interference. Waves in phase are said to resonate, or to be coherent. The electromagnetic wave is called a sine wave in electronic terminology. One wavelength is equal to the length of one whole crest and one whole dip.

A traveling train of waves has a frequency that equals the number of its crests that pass a given point per second. Thus, for my

300-kilocycle station (1 kilocycle = 1,000 cycles) in Ireland, 300,000 cycles, or sine waves passed over a point on the surface of the Earth each second. Mathematically then, if wavelength (λ) = the speed of light divided by the frequency, then the velocity (speed) of the wave equals wavelength times frequency; or in the case of my radio range station in Ireland, mentioned in the last chapter, velocity = 300 kilocycles x 1,000 meters = 300,000 kilometers per second, or the speed of light. Now we see why it is so important to have accurate measurements of the speed of light. In 1907, Albert Michelson was the first American to receive a Nobel Prize in Science. He received it for measuring very accurately the speed of light with his Michelson interferometer. Today, scientists utilizing a hydrogen-cyanide laser are calculating a light-speed constant that is 100-fold more accurate than previous values. They are looking at a reproducibility of one part in 10,000 billion (10 in 10^{13}).

In the spectral region of the long waves of my radio range station, or of Tesla's Earth waves, great accuracy is not necessary; but, at the present time, we are working at the other end of the spectrum where light and IR wavelengths are measured in micrometers (one-thousandth of a millimeter) or even nanometers (one-thousandth of a micrometer). If we are going to look at "tuned" or resonant circuits in these regions, we need to know the speed of light to a much greater degree of accuracy.

If you look at a regular light bulb, the electrons that make up the rays reaching your eyes are not marching together in phase. They are all going out in different directions, and at different times. The emitted electrons do not oscillate together in harmony. Waves that do not march together are called incoherent waves, as shown in the top of *Figure 5*. Waves that do march together are called coherent waves (bottom of *Figure 5*).

In basic terms, we know what waves and frequency are, but how does one get waves to march together like soldiers? How does one put them in phase so that they resonate? This problem was solved by Tesla for long waves in 1897 with his "tuned circuit." C. H. Townes solved it for very short light waves in 1953 with his gas laser.

There are some admirers of Tesla, and I am one, who suspect that he invented the laser years ago and destroyed it for fear it would become a tool of war. Modern researchers may protest that

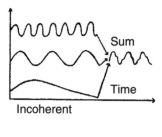

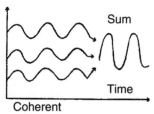

Figure 5. Phase relationship of coherent and incoherent electromagnetic waves. Coherence (*bottom*) implies that at any one instant in time and space the waves will be in phase; that is, that the peaks and dips of each wave will occur simultaneously. Amplification of the signal is inherent in coherent radiation because the waves do not cancel one another.

Incoherent waves (*top*), such as those from a light bulb or other hot bodies (black bodies), are not in phase, so at different times different waves are canceling parts of the other waves.

Tesla never patented a laser. They might maintain that he could not have done so because quantum mechanics had not been invented at that period of science. The argument isn't valid, however, for Thomson discovered the electron before the theory of quantum mechanics was developed. Thomson looked on electrons as raisins buried in a big cake — the atom. He did not have the concept of little packets of energy orbiting around a nucleus, as we view electrons today. There are many who believe, however, that Tesla did invent what he terms a "death ray." Half of any great discovery is hypothesis based on asking the right question. He was known to have had a good grasp of gas discharge phenomena and told of a death ray he invented that could cut through solids. Let me quote from a lecture, "On Light and Other High Frequency Phenomena," delivered at Franklin Institute, Philadelphia (February 1893):

It is very likely that resonant vibration plays a most important part in all manifestations of energy in nature. Throughout space, all matter is vibrating, and all rates of vibration are represented from the lowest musical note to the highest pitch of the chemical rays; hence an atom or complex of atoms, no matter what its period, must find a vibration with which it is in resonance. When we consider the enormous rapidity of the light vibrations, we realize the impossibility of producing such vibrations directly with any apparatus of measurable dimensions, and we are driven to the only possible means of attaining the object of setting up waves of light by electrical means and economically, that is, to affect the molecules or atoms of gas to cause them to collide and vibrate. We then must ask ourselves: How can free molecules or atoms be affected?

The quotation is irrefutable proof that in 1893 Tesla asked the right question about resonating short light waves. He knew that molecular "in phase" waves could not be attained with "apparatus of measurable dimensions;" that is, with coils and condensers as used in the radio region of the spectrum. One would have to put the atoms in resonance to obtain what today we call coherence.

The helium-neon laser, which puts out a coherent in-phase red beam, works on the principle of what laser physicists call "collisions of the second kind" between two dissimilar gases. At any finite pressure, the lifetime of any radiation emission will be significantly lengthened by light emitted from atoms being absorbed and re-emitted by other atoms. This is a sort of chain reaction system where re-emittance and reabsorption occur in cycles until, after a number of such cycles, the light escapes as radiation. The stimulus for the radiation from the gas is an electrical discharge, just as Tesla suggested.

It is absolutely inconceivable that a man who knew what Tesla did about gas discharges, light rays, and resonating systems, would not attempt to resonate the output of his gas tubes by some method such as is used in present-day laser research. One would have to be of an extremely selfish nature not to admit the possibility that his "death ray" was a laser.

Tesla never published in scientific journals, and since he considered himself a practical inventor working for humanity, most of his writings are in the form of verbose Victorian essays that were presented before scientific societies. A careful reading of these essays will prove conclusively that he did work on the concept of a laser. John O'Neill, in his biography, says, "Tesla never gave the slightest hint concerning the principles under which the device [death ray] operated." O'Neill, however, was not a scientist, and besides, C. H. Townes had not invented the laser when O'Neill wrote his biography of Tesla in 1944.

One cannot read Tesla's lengthy essays in a critical manner and not admit that, as early as 1893, he had the concept of the laser. Just as resonant circuits of coils and condensers put oscillations of long radio waves in phase and produce coherence, so also do resonating molecules produce coherent light waves. We will never know if, in his later years, Tesla produced a real laser (death ray). He claimed that he did. Whether or not we prefer to believe that Tesla designed a laser, in no way detracts from the genius of Townes, who accomplished the same objective in 1953. There are some who believe that the greatness of one scientist detracts from that of another. This is foolish thinking. Because we show that Tesla was an electrical genius, does not make Townes, or Edison, any less so.

It is interesting that Tesla was experimenting with resonating light waves in gas tubes in 1893, but more to the point that he did patent the first resonant "tuned" circuit in the radio portion of the spectrum.

In 1900, Tesla predicted radio as we know it today. In an essay entitled, "The Problems of Increasing Human Energy," he wrote the following:

> *That communication without wires to any point of the globe is practical with such apparatus would need no demonstration, but through a discovery which I made I obtained absolute certitude. Popularly explained it is exactly this: When we raise the voice and hear an echo in reply, we know that the sound of the voice must have reached a distant wall, or boundary, and must have been reflected from the same. Exactly as the sound, so an electrical wave is reflected, and the same evidence which is afforded by an echo is offered by an electrical phenomenon known as a "stationary" wave — that is, a wave with fixed nodal and ventral regions. Instead of*

sending sound vibrations toward a distant wall, I have sent electrical vibrations toward the remote boundaries of the Earth, and instead of the wall the Earth has replied. In place of an echo I have obtained a stationary electrical wave, a wave reflected from afar.

Tesla was not talking about the "make-and-break" telegraphy of Marconi, but rather about the principle of coherent waves in resonance or, as we say today, *standing waves* on the antenna. As he states, it was a discovery that he made, and it was the single most important concept of what today we call the science of electronics or radio. Of course Hertz, before 1891, knew about standing waves as is evident in his treatise, "Annalen der Physik und Chemi." His resonator transmitter, however, was a small coil, loop antenna, and spark gap. Hertz never believed his system would be useful for long-distance communication. As shown in *Figure 6*, antennas are cut in lengths to match the same wavelength of oscillations being generated or received.

A resonant, or tuned circuit may be a series or a parallel circuit, and is used to electrically shorten or lengthen the antenna. Parallel-tuned circuits (a condenser across a coil instead of at the end of the coil) are used in radio to couple resonant energy from one circuit to another in the transmitter or receiver. For the sake of keeping things simple, however, we will discuss a series-tuned circuit. Series-tuned circuits are often used to electrically "stretch" or "shorten" an antenna or waveguide (transmission lines) so that the length of the antenna or waveguide will match the length of the incoming wave. One would not want to cut or lengthen the antenna every time a different frequency station was tuned to. To accomplish the electrical shortening or lengthening, one places a coil and adjustable condenser in series with the antenna. The antenna then becomes a series-tuned circuit. It might be necessary with a receiver, for instance, to "tune" the antenna electrically to fit waves from four-inches to thirty-three-feet long, as shown in *Figure 6*, or even, as in the case of my radio range, from point-to-point frequencies a few feet long to radio range signals half a mile long. Most antennas are cut to half or quarter wavelengths, for the simple reason that it takes less wire and still works for resonance.

If we look at Tesla's 1897 patent (No. 649,621), we see what looks like nothing more than a couple of coils across an electric

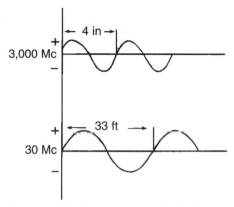

Figure 6. A 3,000-megacycle (1 megacycle = 1,000,000 cycles) radio wave resonates in phase over a 4-inch conducting antenna length. A 30-megacycle radio wave resonates in phase over a 33-foot conducting antenna length.

generator. Actually, his drawings represent a transmitter (see illustration at opening of chapter). For an oscillator (wave producer), Tesla used the AC generator that he invented. This, of course, sends out alternating current in the form of a sine wave. His transmitter consists of a generator across a huge double-loop primary coil. The secondary coil is made of many turns and is grounded at one end. The other end extends upward as a loop antenna. The receiver on the right was a light bulb.

The drawing in the patent does not convey the enormity of this transmitter. Reading the patent does, however, because the loop antenna is of tremendous size, and according to the patent is to be wrapped around a large balloon in the sky. In section 85 of his patent, Tesla tells us that his secondary coil is wound with 50 miles of wire. This includes the loop antenna around the balloon. Since the speed of light is equal to 300,000 kilometers per second, or approximately 186,000 miles per second (we do not have to be very accurate with such long waves), and since Tesla tells us his waves were 200 miles long, then we see his motor was putting out an AC sine wave at:

$$\frac{186,000}{200} = 930 \text{ cycles per second}$$

or a frequency of 930 (200 mile-long) waves per second. This means, in essence, that Tesla was maintaining 930 stationary waves, or sine waves, in his secondary coil. Since his waves are 200 miles long, and his coil only 50, he has in effect a "tuned" quarter-wave transmitting antenna.

At this point, Tesla still is not able to vary wavelengths with his tuned transmitter. Although it is a resonant system, it is fixed to wavelengths 200 miles long, because his 50-mile-long coil and antenna wire are cut to that fixed one-quarter length. His next patent, No. 685953 (filed June 24, 1899) is entitled, "Method of Intensifying and Utilizing Effects Transmitted Through Natural Media." By natural media, Tesla meant air. This second patent is essentially a variable plate condenser utilized to tune the coil and antenna of his transmitter. When Tesla placed this condenser circuit in series with his coil in the transmitter, he had produced a variable tuned circuit, and could resonate quite accurately to many wavelengths by varying the condenser in the circuit.

In electronics, the term *reactance* means opposition to flow of current (the symbol is X). *Capacitive reactance* (X_c) is opposition to current flow offered by capacitors and *inductive reactance* (X_1) by coils. In a tuned circuit, the inductive and capacitive reactance are oppositely affected by frequency. In any series combination of capacitors and coils, there is one particular frequency where capacitive reactance equals inductive reactance $(X_c = X_1)$. The two factors cancel each other out and, at that frequency, for those values the only resistance to the flow of current is that of the wire itself (*Figure 7*).

We see then that by making an adjustable coil or condenser, one can change the values of $X_c = X_1$ to fit any frequency and can thus tune the antenna to different wavelengths. This is the basic circuit for antennas, and for coupling from circuit to circuit in a transmitter or a receiver. All that tubes or transistors do is control the current from these tuned coupling circuits.

As we shall see later, antennas that resonate to short wavelengths, below radio in the infrared and visible regions of the spectrum, may be constructed from insulative substances such as plexiglass, instead of metal. Such a substance is called a dielectric material (Chapter 7). They are cut to exact wavelengths, as our figure shows.

Hertz produced the first long radio waves, and Marconi sent them across distances with his antenna, but it was Tesla who made the whole system work by demonstrating the method by which

Antennae

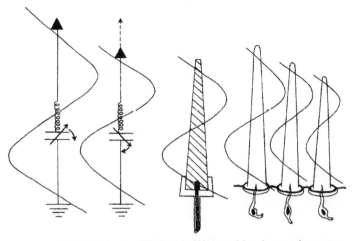

Metal Antenna   Dielectric Waveguide   Insect Antenna
Antenna

Figure 7. To electrically shorten or lengthen a metal antenna (left), a series-tuned circuit is placed in the antenna circuit. Varying (turning) the capacitor of the tuned circuit changes the resonance of the circuit, and thus electrically shortens, or lengthens, a fixed-wire antenna. Dielectric (Chapter 6) waveguide antennae (center) are cut to specific lengths for resonating at specific frequencies. They are tapered for increased efficiency in matching the incoming or outgoing wave. Insect dielectric waveguide antennae tune across a statistical curve of different wavelengths of incoming frequencies, as indicated by the fact that the sensilla of most insects observed occur in step-like lengths across the main branches, or body, of the antennae.

any wave could be controlled at various frequencies. Of course, Tesla was attempting to transmit AC power across space, not to transmit radio signals. He succeeded, for he turned on light bulbs twenty-five miles away. The principles are the same for short or long waves in either case. Tesla should share with Hertz and Marconi the credit for modern electronics — this apart from the fact that he is the real father of our AC power system. It would not seem to diminish the genius of Hertz of Marconi to give Tesla his due credit. In my opinion, Tesla's tuned circuit was the most elegant of the three basic concepts of electronics. (The U.S. Supreme Court does give Tesla credit, as noted in footnote 9, Chapter 2.)

What does the invention of the tuned circuit have to do with insect antennae? At first, the connection may seem quite remote, but now that we know what a tuned circuit is, let us take a closer look at how a laser works. Just as Tesla's tuned circuit puts out gigantic 200-mile-long waves in phase from an AC generator, so a laser puts out tiny short waves in the visible and infrared region from molecular oscillators. Insects are small, so any waves they might detect would have to be very short waves.

The word "laser" comes from the first initials of the words *Light Amplification by Stimulated Emission of Radiation*. Since lasers work by stimulating molecules to oscillate, and can be made to put out both visible or IR radiation, I prefer for my infrared work the term "maser," which means *Micrometer (IR) Amplification by Stimulated Emission of Radiation*. That is why I use that term in this book: insects utilize micrometer radiation. Although insects do detect light radiation (via the compound eyes and ocelli) the mechanism and the morphological structures by which detection is accomplished differ from the mechanism from which micrometer radiation is detected.

As I pointed out before, an electrical discharge is utilized to stimulate emission from a gas laser. Of course, the stimulated emission is nothing more than a form of fluorescence, and the light radiation from the glowing tube is not in phase, and thus not coherent. To attain coherent light from the end of a long glass tube filled with gas, two reflecting mirrors have to be spaced exactly right so that the waves of light, or infrared, will bounce back and forth between them and finally all "get together" in resonance before shooting out the end as a coherent "in-phase" beam. In a later chapter we will look at fluorescence, but for now, suffice it to say that it takes a lot of experimentation to figure out what mixture of gases to use to produce the fluorescence. It also takes rather complex mathematics to arrive at the correct spacing of the reflecting mirrors. Designing lasers is both an art and a science.

The distance between the mirrors is like the distance along the length of the wire antenna: it must be made to match the wavelength that you expect to transmit. There is one main difference, however. Whereas radio antennas are usually half or quarter wavelengths long, laser mirrors may be separated by many wavelengths of distance. Since there is a long space filled with gas between the mirrors, a laser resonating system is called an open resonator or waveguide. We may still consider it a tuned circuit, however, since all the waves are put in phase by "tuning" or spacing the mirrors correctly for the desired frequency, just as the metal antenna is

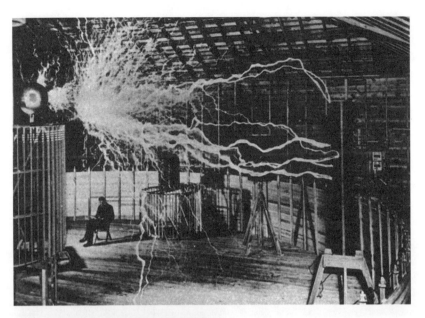

Interior of the Colorado Springs transmitting station. The room is a giant Tesla coil. The lightning bolt is arcing from the three-foot metal ball of the secondary coil to another large coil. The huge primary coil is wound around the curved wooden fence seen in the background. Tesla's technician in the chair indicates the size of the coils. He was photographed first with flash powder, then moved out of the way while the arc was set off to make the double-exposed photograph. (Both photos courtesy of the Nikola Tesla Museum, Belgrade.)

Tesla's experimental transmitting station at Colorado Springs in 1899. Instead of a balloon supporting his antenna, as his patent indicates, he utilized a large metal ball at the end of an 80-foot mast, as shown in this plate.

"tuned" by setting the coil and condenser for the correct reactance ($X_c = X_1$) values to electrically match the wavelength of the radio frequency.

The red coherent beam of a "tuned" helium-neon laser is so intense that it would severely injure your eye if you looked directly at it. You could, of course, see the beam as it gradually burned out your sensitive retina. Since coherent radiation is in phase, it is highly amplified. It may be likened to flicking three jump ropes at another person holding the ropes at the other end. If you flick them one at a time so that a wave moves along each rope, the crests and dips will all arrive at the person at different times, and so the force (mass) of the three ropes will be distributed over a certain time interval at the opposite end. If, however, you flip all three together at one time, the force (mass) of the undulating wave will arrive at the other person's hand simultaneously, and the person holding the end will feel three times the force. That is exactly what tuned radio antennas and lasers do: they "flick" the generated oscillations, from gases in the case of the laser, or from the radio transmitter so that they all leave the transmitter at exactly the same time, and will thus arrive at the receiver at the same time.

In the case of the radio transmitter, the detector of the coherent radiation is your radio receiver or TV set; in the case of the helium-neon laser it is a photocell, or your eye — if one is so foolish. Of course, if you get too close to a high-powered radar or TV antenna , it could damage the tissue of your body as severely as the laser would your eye. The simple fact is that your body would not detect the damage done from high-energy radio as quickly, since you have no built-in receiver for the long radio or radar frequencies, but do for the short light frequencies.

The question we must ask ourselves is: Since man over the last few decades has learned to produce tuned circuits that put out coherent radio, infrared, and visible light, and to detect the frequencies with receivers which also incorporate tuned antennas to resonate to the wavelengths, can such a system already exist in nature? If so, how does such a natural system work, and in which part of the spectrum? I am now certain that such a natural system does exist, and that those most successful of all living organisms, the insects, have evolved the organ for detecting these mysterious frequencies. The paradox of this statement is that I should have spent thirty or so years proving that the insect antenna really is an antenna.

The Fleeting-Floating World

Chapter 4
The Fleeting-Floating World

The Japanese word "Ukiyo," although difficult to interpret by Western standards, is best translated as "the fleeting-floating world." Applied to many things Japanese, in particular to the period of Japanese art in which the woodcut was developed, the word describes the inherent feeling of the Japanese people for small things and minute detail — more important, with the illusive world of transitory things, the world felt by the spirit rather than seen by the eyes.

Indeed, the love of the Japanese for smallness is demonstrated by their miniature gardens, their miniature architecture, their art of dwarfing trees, and by the delight of their children in minute things. For instance, the pet cricket in its diminutive cage brings the same esthetic joy as a dog or a horse brings to an American child. But, as I said before, this feeling for smallness extends beyond mere miniaturization — indeed, it extends into things that cannot be seen — into a transient world which the Japanese, through their literature and traditions, believe to exist, but which we in the West sometimes overlook. I believe that what I am about to discuss might be described as the fleeting-floating world — the "Ukiyo" of entomology. If anything can be described as "fleeting-floating," it is certainly airborne molecules and the unique and subtle electromagnetic infrared "colors" that they emit. One bright summer day in England, I was given a fleeting look at this fleeting-floating world.

Close by the edge of the Dartmoor, of fame in some many English novels, is the village of Chagford. Chagford is located where the river Teign branches north and south. The south branch of the river has its source at Fernworthy marsh in the wild desolate north central highlands of the moor. It is near here where the ghostly hound of the moors terrorized the Baskervilles of the famous Sherlock Holmes detective story. In that mystery classic we read that the great black snarling dog murdered the Baskervilles by attacking from the sanctuary of a rocky tor.

The Dartmoor overlies a granite mass called a "boss." Along with four other bosses, the Dartmoor boss is the base of south-western England. Bosses are the stumps of a mountain system formed millions of years ago, since leveled by geologic processes. The unique masses of stone called tors are the caps of unrotted piles of granite on the hills. They have been strangely sculptured and weathered by the fierce winter winds that sweep across the open moors.

In 1964, I was in England at the 12th International Congress of Entomology. When the meeting was over, my love of hiking took me to the wind-swept Dartmoor. I left Chagford with my rucksack early in the morning, and noontime found me eating lunch at Watern tor. The sun was high, and the meeting forgotten. The sight of a merlin sweeping across the rolling hills, the charm of clapper bridges, huge flat stones that reach across the heather-lined brooks, and the delicate moorland cover of pale butterwort and bog pimpernel, all united in a silent conspiracy to wipe science from my mind.

As I lay on my back in the shade of the tor, the white cumulus clouds piled up in the background, and the flat top of the ridged, granite tor floated in and out of sunlight and shadows like a boat tossed about on the rolling waves of the moorland. The silence of the moorland pervaded those wild hills even in daylight, and was conducive to daydreaming. As my mind wandered here and there among nostalgic memories, I suddenly became aware of some peculiar black spots dancing against the sky. At first I thought I had spots in front of my eyes, but a closer look revealed thousands of small insects flying and hovering over the top of the rocky tor. They appeared to be flies, so I turned to the chapter on the natural history of Dartmoor in the park guide of the region. Sure enough, L. A. Harvey, who wrote the chapter, reported that in fine

A rocky tor on the Dartmoor. The heated top of the dark rocks attracts flies (*Diptera*).

summer weather many forms of *Diptera* (flies) and other species of insects are attracted to the tops of the tors. He wrote further that while entomologists have been interested in the manner in which insects are attracted to these heights, neither the cause nor the full extent of the strange phenomenon has yet been determined.

I climbed the steep side of the tor and placed my hand on the top surface. It had been warmed by the summer sun. The black rock had absorbed the hot infrared rays of the sun and was retransmitting them back into space. Heat and infrared radiation are considered one and the same by most. In fact, often as not, say infrared radiation and the usual reply is, "Oh, you mean heat." Of course I do, and yet I don't, and it will take the rest of this book to straighten out that statement. Many species of insects seek warm pockets of air, concerned, for one reason or another, with their thermal equilibrium or behavior. This, of course, is the obvious explanation for the swarming attraction of the flies to the heated surface of the tor, just as light is the obvious explanation for the attraction of a moth to a candle flame. The unfortunate thing about the obvious explanation, however, is that it is not necessarily the whole explanation, or, for that matter, the correct explanation. One is often misled by the obvious. It is true that, with the heat detectors in my hand, I could sense the temperature of the rocks, and yet temperature has inherent in its very being the infrared frequencies that I could never sense directly. These radiations are as invisible as cosmic rays to human senses, and yet it is this invisible infrared radiation that illuminates our bodies day or night.

What the warm top of the tor, or a candle, means to my mind is not heat or visible light. Both are generators of tremendous amounts of infrared energy — a sort of invisible fleeting-floating energy world that we barely understand — a world where mists of molecules from the candle, or above the hot rock, glow like various colors of fluorescent neon lights. We might term these glows "invisible St. Elmo's fire."

St. Elmo's fire is the eerie visible glow that accompanies the brushlike discharge of atmospheric electricity sometimes appearing as a ball of light at the tip of a pointed object like a church tower, or the mast of a ship. On dark stormy nights, St. Elmo's fire probably accounts for more ghost stories and tales of apparitions than does any other natural phenomenon. I have seen this ghostly corona discharge around the periphery of aircraft propellers when flying in the vicinity of an ice storm over northern Hokkaido. The name for the eerie glow comes from ancient sailors in the Mediterranean region. "St. Elmo" is a corruption of St. Erasmus, the patron saint of sailors. On storm nights, the glow of the light, forming a cross at the tip of the spars and mast, was considered a good omen.

We, of course, know about St. Elmo's fire because we can see the spooky visible glow with our own eyes. If a similar glow occurred in the infrared region of the spectrum, we would not name it anything for the simple reason that we would not see it. In the case of St. Elmo's glow, high charges of atmospheric electricity stimulate the molecules of air to break into ions around the steeple and to glow, or fluoresce, as we say, and emit visible light. The church steeple acts as an electrode to focus the electrical energy onto the molecules of air surrounding the steeple. The phenomenon might be looked upon as a sort of free, uncontained fluorescent light bulb.

The simple fact, however, is that a much lesser amount of energy than the electricity from a storm can stimulate molecules of almost any vapor surrounding almost any object to "glow" infrared wavelengths in some region of the spectrum. We would

St. Elmo's fire from a stink bug. This eerie glow was created by the author in his lab utilizing a high frequency Tesla coil at 3,000 V per square centimeter field potential. Since the insect is in a voltage field insulated from the coil, there is no current present; the insect is not harmed and lives on normally. Any insect can be lighted up in this manner. The voltage potentials under thunder heads, or in certain atmospheric conditions where there are ice crystals or pollution particles in the air, can be as high as 3,000 V per square centimeter of air space. This leads the author to believe that many of the UFO sightings at night are mass swarms of lighted insects migrating and caught in just such a voltage field between the sky and Earth.

never know it because our eyes are not "tuned" to it. In certain cases, even solid objects fluoresce in the infrared, and thus cannot be seen within the narrow limits of our vision. Only a few years ago it was learned that corn plants fluoresce at one micrometer infrared when radiated by visible light. If we could see in that region of the IR spectrum, the whole corn field would appear by moonlight as a vast array of fluorescent light bulbs sticking up out of the soil. It is just such unknown mysteries of nature as these that space research will uncover for us. The entomologist and the space scientist must form a new and firm partnership to study nature's secrets together.

I climbed down from the tor and started for Cranmere Pool. A storm was brewing in the west, but the sun still beat down on the flat-topped rock. I could see the dancing specks above the dark silhouette of the tor.

From the wild moorland surface around the ancient pile of rocks there rises a mysterious mist of vapors called scents. They float over the tor from the straggly bushes of heather; from the purple moor grass, the bog cotton, the mosses and lichens, the sweat of scraggy moorland ponies, the odors of lapwings and curved-beak curlews, and even from my own tired body. This multitude of vapors mixes in the air and floats like an effervescent mist over the heated surface of the rocks. The sun beating down on the tor reflects its energy back up into the great swirling brew of vapors. At night the moon, sky and starlight all radiate the same mass of molecular mists. As the vapors drift across the rocks from the heather-covered moorland, the molecules making up the vapors vibrate, bend and rotate as they absorb the hot rays. This stimulates them to oscillate at many unknown frequencies of colors — not visible colors of red or blue or green, but infrared "colors" of much longer wavelengths. If we had infrared eyes, we would give names to these colors — these auras of beautifully psychedelic infrared frequencies, as easily tuned to by an antenna as are the visible colors by the rods and cones of our eyes.

Were the flies over the tor attracted to these infrared vapor "colors" from plant scent molecules? The scents must be stimulated to emit the "colors" by the sun's energy reflecting on the molecules from the heated pile of rocks. Is an insect antenna really an antenna tuned to these subtle frequencies? It appeared to be the same phenomenon as moth attraction to my gas mercury vapor transmitter tubes that I had observed years before in Ireland.

What I saw in my mind against the blackening sky were infrared "colors" of a creation so strange, so mysterious, so wonderfully one of God's great secrets that we are not yet able to "tune" with any kind of efficiency to its millions of vibrating frequencies.

As I walked away, I was certain that such frequencies exist, and that the insect senses them with its antenna. The question I was asking myself was, how does the insect antenna "tune" to, or "resonate" to those narrowband infrared colors? I did not even consider that it could not do so. If, as in the case of ESP research, I had to spend my life trying to prove that insects do detect infrared radiation, I would never live long enough to prove how they detect it. Once I knew how they detect the radiation, proving that they do detect it would take care of itself.

As I reached Cranmere Pool and turned for the shelter of Chagford Inn, the sudden summer storm swept across the moorlands. The sky blackened and a cold wind ripped at the rucksack on my back. When I reached the inn, I dried off and sipped wine before the huge fireplace. The flickering light of the burning peat played across my eyes. The great gray fireplace lifted the yellow darts of warmth and flung them against my cold body. I wonder why an open fire stirs such hypnotic longings in the hearts of men. It is a yearning brought about only by the radiations of a fire. An electric light is a dead luminosity, but a dancing fire is a living light.

All that we can see is the visible radiation, but the fire is the generator, the transmitter, the oscillator of many thousands of invisible frequencies that we, in our ignorance of nature, lump under the single term of heat. In front of that fireplace, more than heat reached my body. It is as if we human beings still have the remains of some mysterious ability to perceive the invisible fleeting-floating world of the infrared fire — an ability inherited from a more simple organism from which we ourselves may have evolved millions of eons ago.

Tuning In To Moths

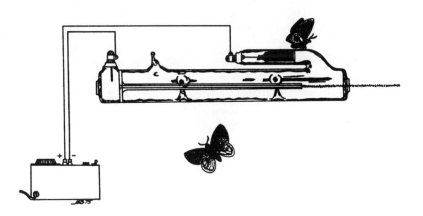

Chapter 5
Tuning In To Moths

When Nikola Tesla put together his giant tuned circuits, he did not have to worry about whether the long wavelength frequencies would transmit through the air. Even if he had known about water vapor windows, the low frequency radio waves are of such lengths that the tiny molecules of water vapor in the air do not absorb the long wavelengths. However, if one is to look for tiny waves from tiny molecular frequency oscillators, or from hot bodies, then it is obvious that those frequencies likely to be utilized in a communication system — an insect system for instance — must, of necessity, transmit through the air. Because water vapor absorbs and scatters infrared frequencies in some regions, but lets it through in other regions, called windows, we must concentrate on tuning to molecular infrared frequencies in the water vapor windows.

In 1965 I wrote a paper entitled, "Intermediate and Far Infrared Sensing of Nocturnal Insects: Part I — Evidence for a Far Infrared Electromagnetic Theory of Communication and Sensing in Moths and Its Relationship to the Limiting Biosphere of the Corn Earworm Moth."

By biosphere, scientists mean that part of the world in which life can exist. One of the reasons that life can exist on Earth is intimately related to the 7- to 14-micrometer water vapor window.

By limiting biosphere, I was referring mainly to this important infrared window. The transmission of IR radiation through the air from the sun depends on the concentration and types of gaseous molecules composing our atmosphere, which in turn depend on weather conditions in the lower atmosphere. The transmission of IR radiation in the atmosphere varies considerably with both weather conditions and altitude. There are, in addition to the main gases of nitrogen and oxygen that compose air, many important trace atmospheric gases other than water vapor. These gases include carbon dioxide, methane, ozone, carbon monoxide and nitrous oxide. They all absorb various frequencies from the sun. Ozone absorbs most of the UV radiation. Water vapor, however, is the most important gas, and we need only consider it for the present.

Relative humidity is a measure of the ratio of the amount of water vapor in a given volume of air to the maximum amount possible at a given temperature. At any given temperature, the greater the number of molecules of water per cubic centimeter of air space, the more IR radiation is absorbed. However, the 7- to 14-micrometer window lets most of the IR radiation wavelength between those limits reach the Earth where it is absorbed on the surface. If the Earth were not able to reradiate the heat associated with this wide band of frequencies back out into space, it would eventually absorb more and more heat until it reached an intolerable temperature. Fortunately, the same 7- to 14-micrometer window that lets the IR radiation reach the Earth all day long, allows it to reradiate back from the warm surface of the globe all day and all night long. The excess heat is lost to the surface of the Earth as it reradiates back into space.

Scientists call such heated bodies as the Earth, black bodies. A radiating black body is any heated body that absorbs all radiation and radiates infrared wavelengths in a range that depends on its peak temperature. Different black bodies have different peaks of radiation wavelengths, depending on their temperatures. In general, the hotter the body, the shorter the peak-radiation wavelengths; the cooler the body, the longer the wavelengths (see *Figure 8*). Since the sun is very hot, it emits frequencies that peak at very short wavelengths in the visible spectrum. The Earth's surface seldom reaches an average temperature of more than 70° to 100° F and therefore peaks at a wavelength of approximately 10 micrometers in the 7- to 14-micrometer window. It is this curve of the peak Earth temperature that reradiates back out into space.

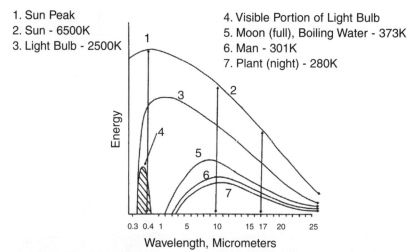

1. Sun Peak
2. Sun - 6500K
3. Light Bulb - 2500K

4. Visible Portion of Light Bulb
5. Moon (full), Boiling Water - 373K
6. Man - 301K
7. Plant (night) - 280K

Wavelength, Micrometers

Figure 8. The black body infrared radiation peaks for various hot bodies. Anything above -270°C is "hot." The absolute temperature (K) of a body is its temperature in centigrade +270°C. The sun at 6500K peaks in the visible region. A light bulb at 2500K in the near infrared at approximately 1μm. Note that very little of the total energy of a light bulb is visible, but rather infrared radiation out to 25 or 30μm. Most warm-bodied animals and plants peak at around 10μm in the 7 to 14μm atmospheric window.

Besides the natural hot and warm bodies of nature, there are, of course, man-made hot objects. Hot automobile engines, factories, tungsten-filament light bulbs, the heated pavement of cities — many more. All are black bodies emitting an infrared radiation peak at the peak of their own temperatures.

A tungsten filament heated to 2500°K (K is the symbol for absolute temperature) glows visible white light, so is called white heat. As the temperature is lowered, the wavelength becomes longer and moves toward the longer invisible wavelengths in the infrared frequency range. If you lower the voltage in a filament, it will glow red as the wavelengths move toward the red and infrared frequencies. Lower it still more and it will still be hot, but the red will disappear, for it will have moved completely away from the visible frequencies into the invisible IR at cooler temperatures. Of course, even the visible light bulb filament is giving off far more radiation in the near infrared region of the spectrum than in the visible region. It is a simple fact that very little of the total radiation from a tungsten light bulb lies in the visible range. Most is lost as infrared radiation, and is not detectable by our eye.

In 1856, the English astronomer, Sir William Herschel, began experimenting with sunlight and color. He used a prism to spread the colors from sunlight across the spectrum — from violet at the shorter wavelengths, through green, yellow and orange, to red at the longer wavelengths. He observed, much to his surprise, that when he laid a thermometer in the various radiation colors, although yellow was the brightest, red was much the hottest. When he moved the thermometer past the visible red to where his eye could see no radiation, the thermometer recorded the

Sir William Herschel, the discoverer of infrared radiation.

highest temperature. This radiation that Herschel discovered is now recognized as the portion of the spectrum emitted by all hot objects, and called infrared black body radiation. Herschel postulated that the "hot" radiation was of the same nature as light and termed it "invisible light." His ideas about this strange invisible radiation, which we now know were right, were vigorously disputed for over half a century.

The German physicist, Wilhelm Wien, determined a mathematical calculation to figure where the peak of radiation for any hot body lies. Using this constant, one can figure the wavelength of radiation associated with the peak temperature of any heated object. Thanks for the astute mathematical calculations of Wien, it is not necessary to be a physicist to know the frequency of a hot body. The magic constant, called Wien's constant, is 2897. If we take this number and divide it by the absolute temperature of any object, we get the wavelength associated with the peak temperature. Absolute temperature is always the degrees of the body in centigrade, plus 270°. Zero on the absolute scale is -270° centigrade, (the precise number is -273.16, but I rounded if off for ease of calculation), so we have to add 270°.

A human body with a skin temperature of 96° F (which equals 36° on the centigrade scale) will equal 36° C plus 270°, or an absolute temperature of 306° K. The symbol for absolute temperature, now called Kelvin's (after Lord Kelvin), is K. Therefore,

$$\text{wavelength} = \frac{2897}{301°K} = 9.47 \text{ micrometers}$$

which means the waves are 9.47 micrometers long.

Now we see that the human body emits infrared radiation at a peak of 9.47 micrometers. It is obvious that 96° Fahrenheit — 36° on the Centigrade scale — is not very hot. We certainly do not burn ourselves if we touch another person's skin. One might say that we are designed to live at this temperature, and at this skin peak frequency of 9.47 micrometers. This is what I call natural radiation.

Let me emphasize again that just as the sun is a 6500°K black body emitting short visible (white hot) wavelengths, the human body is a much cooler black body that emits very long IR wavelengths which peak at 9.47 micrometers. Using Wien's constant, we can easily make a list of the peak infrared radiations of common objects — either man-made or natural. Remember that anything over 0°K (-270°C) is "hot."

From Table 1 it becomes quite obvious that all things natural to the Earth radiate naturally in the infrared. Why, then, do we not spend more time researching this part of the spectrum?

As with the case of all of the above objects, a night-flying moth — or any other insect for that matter — is a hot body. Every insect, mammal, tree, weed, and living creature emits its own characteristic black body radiation.

When I first started as an agricultural researcher, I began to study the life history, biology and radiation requirements of the corn earworm moth. Before it's name was changed to *Helicoverpa zea*, the scientific Latin name for this important economic pest of corn, cotton, tomatoes, and a host of other crops was *Heliothis zea* from the Greek word *heliotis* – of the sun (or dawn) — and *zea* for corn.

Why it was originally named for the sun — or more accurately, the sunrise — I am unable to explain. It sits quietly all day long and, in fact, ceases flying at dawn. It is a night-flying moth from the family *Noctuidae*, an appropriate family name for the group

Table 1

Peak Temperature and Associated
Infrared Radiations of Emitting Hot Bodies

From Wien's Constant

Emitter	Centigrade Temperature		Absolute Temperature K	Peak Wavelength In Micrometers
Sun	6230 + 270	=	6500	0.45 (green light)
Light bulb	2230 + 270	=	2500	1.16 (near IR)
Moon (full)	103 + 270	=	373	7.77 (far IR)
Human skin	36 + 270	=	306	9.47 (far IR)
Plant (day, 75°)*	24 + 270	=	294	9.85 (far IR)
Plant (night, 65°)	18 + 270	=	288	10.06 (far IR)

*Temperature in degrees F.

because the word "noctuid" is traditionally derived from the Latin word for owl but has since come to mean more generally, and more simply, "night". We call moth members of the night-flying noctuid family owlet moths. The second or species part of the scientific name, *zea*, is appropriate since the corn ear is the moths's favorite site for the oviposition of the eggs (oviposition is the biologist's term for egg laying). Corn is also the preferred food of the larva form. The egg is deposited on the corn silk and the tiny larva (corn earworm), when it hatches, migrates down the silk to the tip of the ear where it feeds and eventually grows to maturity.

The corn earworm is a fascinating night-flying creature, and I have studied its behavior for quite a few years. Not only is the corn earworm fascinating as one of God's creatures, but, of all insects, it is certainly one of the most destructive to agricultural crops. It is, therefore, of tremendous economic importance to mankind. The corn earworm is attracted to the fruiting parts of the plants, and although the corn ear is its favorite food, it will survive on the fruit of almost any crop or weed. There is a list of more than forty host plants for this insect, and at least one third of them are agricultural crops. This moth (or its near relatives in Europe and Asia), is estimate to destroy billions of dollars worth of crops all over the world. There are very few agricultural entomologists who would not list this insect as among the top ten destructive insect pests in the world.

The larva of a moth is an eating machine. It feeds and stores food in preparation for its adult life as, in reality, nothing more than a flying, egg-laying, reproductive machine. The worm begins life on leaving the eggs as a small larva less than one millimeter in length; it grows through five or six molts to a length of approximately 43 millimeters (1.5 inches). Then it goes through the change of form that biologists call metamorphosis. Before the corn earworm makes the transformation from larva to pupa, it leaves the corn plant and burrows a few inches into the soil where it undergoes the change to the quiescent pupal form. Depending on temperature, it may spend from ten to twenty days in the soil. The adult moth emerges at night from the soil and seeks a sheltered spot to expand and dry its wings. Adult moths live from eight to fifteen days at summer temperatures. During this reproductive stage they are faced with two major communication problems. To

A corn earworm moth attracted to a window illuminated with broadband 0.9 to 15μm black body IR radiation. Since the radiation is neither modulated nor narrowband, it is not particularly attractive to the moth. However, the moth does investigate it. The thin antennae shown here are the supports for the thousands of microminiature sensilla (spines) which detect the infrared radiation emitted by molecules.

mate, the male must first locate a female; then the female must find the proper host plant for oviposition.

In a moth communication system — or in any organism's communication system — we must distinguish between what we term a guidance system and an attractance system. A guidance system tells the insect in which direction to orientate, and an attractance system is the message that directs the fulfillment of some biological urge inherent to the species. For example, if we are thirsty and are hiking across the desert at night and see a distant light, we guide on the light. The eye and the light bulb, interacting together, are the guidance system. At the same time, however, our computer brain tells us that in all probability there is a house, and perhaps water where the house is located. The water is the attractant force. Of course we might get close enough not only to see the light, but also to hear the babbling brook near by. The sound of the brook is a powerful attractant message to the thirsty, but the point source of light is still the best guidance system in the dark.

However, one signal may include both the guidance factor and the attractant factor. One could guide on the sound of the brook even if there were no light, providing one were close enough to hear the brook. A blind person could easily find the brook, because both messages are inherent in the sound. The blind person, though, might be out of luck if he were too far away to hear the brook. On the other hand, the point source of light could be viewed by the eye from ten miles across the desert. The point source of light is by far the better navigational signal, because not only does it travel in a straight line, but the eye can also orient to it over large distances.

Electromagnetic radiation as an orientating, or attractant, signal can be either broadband or narrowband. White light contains all of the frequencies of the visible spectrum: violet, blue, green, yellow, orange and red. The white light on a ship tells us that an object is ahead in the sea. This is a broadband signal. As we approach the ship, we see a red light on the port side (left side of ship), and green light on the starboard side (right side of ship). Those two narrowband signals modify our behavior in respect to the approaching ship. The two different narrowband radiations tell us that the ship is approaching from our left or right side.

If we are approaching at right angles to the ship ahead, and can see the green light on the right side of the ship, then we know that we have the right-of-way and can cross its path. If the two ships are approaching dead on, the both steer to the right so that their red (left) lights are visible as they pass in the dark. These two narrowband electromagnetic radiations tell us a lot more than does the white light alone. We have split up the frequencies so that we get more of what scientists call "bits" of information from the radiation.

We can impose more "bits" of information on either broadband or narrowband radiations. For instance, we may blink the white light from the bridge and break it into dots and dashes so that many bits of information are transmitted. This superimposition of information on a transmitted signal is called "modulation." We modulate, or change, the carrier wave of the white light beam by a make-and-break modulator — a blinker shutter. The beam itself is called the "carrier" wave, because it carries the modulated signal. Make-and-break modulation is the most elementary form devised by man, and has been used since the beginning of recorded history — *e.g.*, in the smoke signal or heliograph mirror.

You will remember from our table that the white light comes from a black body tungsten filament heated to 2,500 degrees absolute temperature. A resting moth, however, is a cold-blooded insect — his temperature is the same as that of his environment. A corn earworm moth sitting on a corn leaf in the cornfield at night has a body temperature of approximately 68°F, if the night temperature is 68°F. As in the case of the lights of Tateyama by daylight — viewed from the deck of my yellow junk — the moth radiation frequency associated with the peak of 68°F temperature could not be detected. Since the radiation from the moth is the same as the night background radiation, it is lost in the background radiation. The radiations are too close together to separate one from the other. The lights of Tateyama came into view not because the light from the tungsten bulbs changed, but rather because the sun slowly sank, changing the background radiation so the lights could be viewed as point sources against the cooler night background radiation.

When a night-flying moth arouses from its daylight quiescent period, it engages in a very peculiar behavioral sequence. It unfolds its wings from the resting position. (Unlike butterflies that fold their wings together vertically above their bodies, moths' wings are folded in a tent-shaped position against the sides of the thorax and abdomen. Butterflies keep their antennae extended in front of the head, but moths at rest fold them back under the tent-shaped wings.) As the moth spreads its wings, the antennae are moved forward, and the horizontally held wings begin to slowly vibrate at high frequency. The amplitude of vibration (arc of sweep) is very low, and since the frequency is high — up to 50 cycles per second — it is difficult to see the wings vibrating. In low night light, the vibration cannot be observed at all, but under day-light conditions the delicate wing markings appear blurred. The moth may be thought of as warming up its engines for flight. An insect flaps its wings by vibrating the thoracic muscles, which in turn vibrate the wings, the high-frequency thoracic vibration gen-erating a considerable amount of metabolic heat in the body of the insect. This process, and the aerodynamics of insect flight, are explained in detail in my book, *Insects and How They Function*.

After about a minute or so of low amplitude vibrations, the moth takes flight. At that moment, the vibrations which have gradually increased in amplitude reach their maximum flight sweep and the wings are making large arcs on each side of the body, the heat of which in the corn earworm may rise as high as 8°F above the temperature of the moth at rest. A large sphingid moth, such as the white-lined sphingid, reaches a temperature of more than 18°F above its resting temperature. A female moth receptive to mating sits in one spot and vibrates her wings.

Using Wien's constant (see Table 1) we see that the Earth and its covering of plants peaks at a radiation of 9.85 micrometers dur-ing a 75°F (24°C) day. Night-flying moths seek their mates at night when the temperatures range around 65°F (18°C) and the plant and Earth background radiation peaks at approximately 10.34 microm-eters. However, the vibrating moth is not at 65°, but 8°F above the night sky, at a body temperature of 73°F. At 73°F, the peak infrared wavelength is 9.88 micrometers. We see that as the body heat of the moth increases, the wavelength peak of its black body infrared radi-ation moves to a shorter peak wavelength. It moves from 10.34 micrometers, which is the background and resting moth wave-length peak, to 9.88 micrometers, which contrasts against the back-ground peak of 10.34 like a light bulb. Insects are not truly either warm- or cold-blooded, because their temperature changes with their activity. A true cold-blooded reptile has the same temperature as its environment. Mammals and birds have a built-in temperature control system and remain at one temperature regardless of the change in temperature in the environment.

Those who throw the word ecology around and do not understand the relationship between temperature, infrared radiation, and the environmental infrared windows, also do not really understand the science of ecology. I have explained black body radiation in detail, for it is basic to all ecological systems and is in reality rather easy to understand. One does not have to be a physicist to develop a feeling for such basic relationships. I once had a chemistry professor who taught his freshman course as though it were an advanced graduate class of Ph.D. candidates. Of course ninety percent of his class failed, for he did not impart to us an understanding of the basics of his subject. I never took another chemistry course, unfortunately, but learned chemistry by reading books on the subject. Such a professor is not a teacher, but one whose egotism overshadows his common sense. Fortunately there were not many teachers of this sort, although every school has a few. Most instructors begin with basic concepts and gradually work the students up through complex details.

Once a moth starts vibrating, it is for all practical purposes an infrared firefly. We know that a firefly flashes on and off, for we can see the flashes at night. To "see" our corn earworm infrared firefly, however, requires a rather complex infrared detection system called a bolometer. In 1967, I succeeded in "tuning in" to a corn earworm with a rather crude bolometer. Since then I have done so much more efficiently with newly discovered infrared detectors.

For certain reasons that have to do with electronics, it is much easier to amplify on an AC (alternating sine wave) signal than a steady DC signal. A moth that is vibrating its wings is heated up and consequently emits like a light bulb. When the moth starts vibrating, the wing amplitude is low, so the wings are not chopping the body radiation — that is, they are not cutting the moth body radiation on and off like a signal blinker. The emitted IR light is not being modulated by the wings, so the emitted DC signal is steady — like a steady light source. Once the wings reach an amplitude where they move up and down across the hot thoracic region, they are "chopping" or modulating the peak IR black body output. Such a system carries a much more complex message, because the carrier black body frequency is modulated like a blinker light. It is also easier to amplify because it is not a steady DC signal, but rather an alternating AC signal.

When I first succeeded in setting up a system to tune to this low-energy infrared signal from a moth, my old bolometer did not have a fast response time. The detector in the electronic system could "see" the body radiation, but it could not "see" the change in the signal from the vibrating wings modulating the signal. To put it simply, by the time the detector picked out the IR light at the top of the beat, the wing would already be on the way to the bottom of the downward sweep. Put another way, if we place a light behind a fan blade, the light appears as a steady glow to our eye because the blade is turning too fast for our eye to respond. If we slow the fan blade down gradually, it reaches speed that produces an alternating signal as each blade alternately blocks the light to our eye. If we could make our eye respond faster, we would see the off-on flicker at much higher chopping frequencies.

Not long ago, physicists developed an infrared detector called a pyroelectric detector. It is made from a small crystal of a chemical known as triglycinesulphate. Glycine is an amino acid found in all higher living organisms. There are large amounts of it in the exoskeleton of insects. We may consider triglycinesulphate as a biological infrared detector. Not only is it highly sensitive to weak infrared signals, but it works very well at room temperatures — in other words, at *natural* temperatures. Older detectors had to be cooled down with liquid helium and consequently were extremely expensive and complex. Pyroelectric detectors also respond at high speed in microseconds (millionths of a second) instead of milliseconds (thousandths of a second) as did the older detectors. Pyroelectric detectors respond to minute changes in temperature. The change in temperature is recorded by a change in capacitance. The change can be amplified and also converted to the radiation frequency associated with each temperature recorded.

When I finally put together a system utilizing a triglycinesulphate detector, I discovered that insects do emit a coded infrared signal, and that my theory that it contained a unique navigational message was indeed correct.

The signal I displayed on an oscilloscope (see *Figure 9*) showed that it had all the characteristics of what we old Air Force types call an *Instrument Landing System* (ILS). Since most of the insect's IR radiation is from the thorax, and very little from the head of abdomen, the highest intensity signal is from the side (*Figure 9a*).

As a moth was rotated slowly for a five-second period in front off the detector, the signal intensity rose from a 0, dead ahead, to a maximum of eight millivolts (each square on the display equals one millivolt) at 90° from the side, then to a low of two millivolts from off the rear end of the abdomen at 180° (*Figure 9a*). The hor-

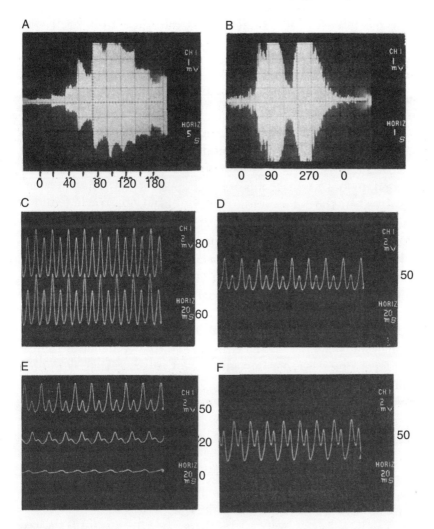

Figure 9. Oscilloscope recordings of the wing flapping "hot" broadband black body infrared radiation from a flying corn earworm moth. See text and drawing for an explanation of the compass (azimuth) and glide path (height) vectors.

izontal sweep of time in seconds is recorded at the bottom right of the display figure, and the millivolt signal (strength) for each square of the grid, at the top left above the horizontal time sweep.

When I rotated the moth quickly in one second 360° around in front of the detector (*Figure 9b*), the signal went from zero millivolts at the head, to a maximum of eight millivolts on the right side, and back down to two millivolts at 180°, than up again to eight millivolts 270°; decreasing again at the head, demonstrating that the intensity of the signal was the same from each side. Cutting off the moth's wing on one side caused the signal to disappear on that side, indicating that the slapping wings were indeed modulating the signal. The pair of wings on each side were acting as the chopping blades of a modulation system — like the fan blade in front of the light bulb.

Since my triglycinesulphate detector could see a signal at a fast-time domain, I parked a moth in front of the detector and speeded the oscilloscope sweep up to 20 milliseconds ($^{20}/_{1000}$ of a second) to look at the details of the chopped signal. The results are displayed in the four bottom figures. Starting at 0° (*Figure 9e*), there is practically no signal, but at 20°, 50°, 60°, and 80° (*Figures 9e and 9c*), the signal gradually increases in intensity (amplitude). The signal has a decidedly characteristic two-wave form. These displays were all taken with each grid square equal to two millivolts; consequently, I could get two or three sweeps on each screen to compare them. As the moth is rotated in steps in front of the detector from 0° to 80°, the signal increases and is shown to have a small side peak next to the large main peak. As the moth angle is changed for each recording, the height of the side peak (amplitude) rises until, at 90°, it equals the main peak in height. At this position, the number of total waves has changed from eight waves in 20 milliseconds of sweep (0 degrees) to 16 (double the number) off the side at 90°. The small side peak gradually grows in amplitude from 0° to 90° until it equals the main peak. All of these scans were taken at three o'clock, horizontal to the moth. Notice what happens to the signal at 50°, for instance, when the detector is raised to two o'clock high above the side of the moth. In *Figure 9d* the small peak sits right on the base line. In the display below (*Figure 9f*) the detector has been moved up to two o'clock above the moth and the small side peak has moved up from the base line so that it now begins half way up the main peak.

We can see that by looking at my oscilloscope display I can determine the position of the moth by reading out both the intensity of the signal from any point around 30°, and by observing the size of the side peak's amplitude (height) in relation to the main peak. In navigation this is called a compass azimuth reading. Note, however, that by observing the side small peak in relation to the base line and the main peak, I can also tell how far above or below the horizontal the moth is located. In my last display (*Figure 9f*), the detector (male) is above the emitting female moth — or approaching, as we would say in the Air Force, from two o'clock high, and 50° compass azimuth from the side. The characteristic two-peak modulation signal occurs because the moth has two wings on each side, coupled together by a long spine on the hind wing. The spine sticks through a fleshy lobe on the underside of the front wing. This coupling structure on butterflies and moths is called a *frenum*. As the wings move up and down they are held together by the frenum; nevertheless, its looseness allows each wing to twist or change pitch independently of the other. The two wings separate slightly on the down stroke, leaving a gap between the front and hind wing. The shape of the gap is determined by the pitch of each wing at any movement during the stroke. The frequency of beat and placement of the gap at any instant determines the unique IR signal. *Figure 10* is a summary of this moth ILS infrared signal.

This emitted 10-micrometer infrared signal is a perfect navigational device. For another moth to home on such a signal with its antenna, it would have to have a sensor with vectored elements. This means that the antenna elements would need to be arranged in a 360° circle around the main detector. As we shall see in the next chapter, the moth antenna does have such a sensor on it.

Like the visible blinker signal light on the bridge of a ship, this modulated infrared signal is a broadband signal. Just as the visible white light is made up of many lumped narrowband colors, so this broadband infrared signal is made up of many infrared "colors." The signal has all of the wave characteristics of an excellent navigational signal, but it is not likely to be an attractant signal. Even if I could duplicate the signal electronically, I would not be likely to attract a single moth, any more than a light in the desert would attract a thirsty man if he knew there was no water near the light. The male moth might home on this unique signal if some other

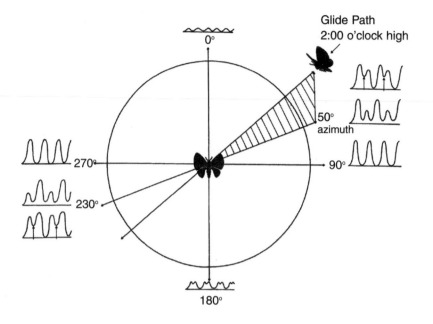

Figure 10. Compass (azimuth) and glide path (height) vector signals from the wing modulated black body infrared radiation of a corn earworm moth. From dead ahead there is little (low amplitude) signals and only eight waves per 20 milliseconds of time ($^{20}/_{1000}$ seconds). At 90° the waves are very large (high amplitude) and there are 16 waves per 20 milliseconds of time. The little side-band peak grows in amplitude as the detector is moved from 0° to 90° around the moth so that at 90° the number of peaks is 16 instead of eight. As the detector is moved above, the little side-band peak also moves up from the baseline so that the signal now appears as notched (2 o'clock high) instead of as separate waves. On the opposite of the moth, the little side-band peak is on the opposite side of the main peak.

messenger told it that the signal came from a female of its own species, and if the female was in the proper state — right age, for instance — to mate with the male. The signal that gives the later message comes from an insect sex attractant. We call it a pheromone from the Greek *pherin* (to carry) and *hormon* (to excite). In other words, a scent chemical that carries a message and excites the moth to mate.

We shall see later how these free-floating chemical messengers also give off infrared, but extremely narrowband, signals rather than broadband signals as in the case of the ILS infrared message from the heated body of the insect. Before we examine the frequency coming from these molecules, however, let us look at the shapes and forms of the spines on the insect antenna. Remember, I believe that form and frequency go together. If this is so, we should be able to look at the shape of the antenna sensor and relate them to frequencies. The invention of a remarkable microscope allowed us to finally get a really close look at the insect antenna.

Form and Frequency

Chapter 6

Form and Frequency

In his fascinating book *My Ivory Cellar*, photographer-scientist John Ott describes his feelings while sitting quietly at night, in the company of his wife, taking time-lapse pictures of the fiery lava flows from the erupting Paricutín volcano in Mexico. Mrs. Ott comments that it was one of the most memorable evenings they had ever spent together.

The author goes on, almost as I did at the beginning of this book, to describe the origin of the universe from the presumed whirling nebula of hot gases. As I read the chapter, I could see Ott in my mind's eye wishing he had been there with his time-lapse camera to record the birth of the universe. Of course, he could but settle for recording another fiery birth — that of a volcano rising from a lonely cornfield in Mexico. His contribution is not only a new and unique scientific technique but, even more important, it gives us a subtle way of looking at life with reference to the development of form in the time span of living things.

Dr. Ott has prepared time-lapse photography for the Disney Studios. We are all familiar with the changing form of clouds, flowers, and other living organisms that have been captured by compressing their spread-out growth onto a single reel of film with Ott's time-lapse technique. Time-lapse photography is not only a beautiful art form, but it also represents a significant contribution to science.

It is important to what I have to say in this book that my readers obtain a view of form, not as it changes with growth, but rather in reference to a particular function of form. I will show you how form relates the antennae of insects to natural electromagnetic infrared frequencies.

This is essentially a technique that Leonardo da Vinci utilized throughout his entire life. Da Vinci's enormous talent as an artist was the same talent that made him an avid student of form. He was a functional morphologist. An appreciation of form makes great artists, but da Vinci's genius went far beyond that into his own natural curiosity about the workings of nature. As he was painting an arm, he asked himself how the muscles of the arm worked. When he painted a bird's wing, he asked what there was about the graceful form that kept the bird aloft. He was not an artist for art's sake alone, for he was a visionary who wondered how nature really works. He was truly a great naturalist.

When da Vinci looked at a bird's wing and then attempted to design a wing that could carry man aloft, he was practicing a science that today we call *bionics*. In bionics, man carefully examines how nature works and then tries to improve his own technology by copying nature. Da Vinci was one of the earliest, and certainly the greatest, practitioner of this science.

What I have been doing in my research might be termed *reverse bionics*. By reverse bionics, I mean that I have carefully analyzed an area of man-made technology, and looked carefully to determine if the same techniques might not already have been utilized by God in His master evolutionary plan for creation. I have long been convinced that there is nothing man-made that does not already exist in nature. Why not electromagnetic antennas?

To really understand how an antenna works, one must also understand the difference between an antenna and a detector of electromagnetic radiation. An antenna is not a detector; it is rather an object that "grabs hold of," or collects, electromagnetic radiation. A detector is the part of an electronic circuit that obtains and converts to a usable form the wave form collected by the antenna.

As we saw in Chapter 2, Nikola Tesla was the man who showed us how to "tune" a long wire, called an antenna, so that it could resonate electrically to the different frequencies "grabbed" out of the air or, conversely, sent out as resonant frequencies in long looping waves across the Earth. The generator of Tesla's waves was his AC generator. In the early days of radio, the first practical receiver of radio waves was the "crystal set." A crystal receiver consists of an antenna, a coil-tuned circuit, and a crystal. The crystal (rock) is the detector that converts the signal, and the long wire antenna and tuned circuit the "collector" of the radio waves. This wire antenna, or collector, besides having the ability to "grab" the waves, also imparts to the receiver, or transmitter, an amplification factor. We have seen with our rope analogy that if all the waves are sent out or collected at the same time, then the energy builds up and a stronger "force" — or in electronic terms, radio energy — is collected by the receiver and sent out by the transmitter.

Antenna design engineers can change the *form* of an antenna and increase the ability of the antenna to "grab hold of" electromagnetic energy. Think for a moment about TV receivers of the past. For those of you old enough to remember the days before cable and satellite dishes, you may recall that if you lived close to a TV station, your set utilized a short "rabbit ear" V antenna to collect the short TV waves out of the air. If you moved farther away from the station, however, you would be forced to put a more complex array of metal bars on your roof to collect the energy. You might have climbed up on the roof and installed a different *shaped* antenna — but you did not modify anything inside the set where the detector-receiver operates. These antennae consisted of all kinds of strange shapes and arrangements of metal bars collecting TV signals from the atmosphere. Some are more efficient than others, depending on their shape and form alone. Certainly nothing else was changed — not the TV sets — and the antennas are all made of metal.

At this point the reader may well have reason to question why I should consider the insect antenna a real antenna. After all, insects are not made of metal. The answer to that question goes back to World War II and the research of some desperate German radar scientists.

Early in the war in Europe, the English developed radar. Many historians credit the invention of radar and its effective utilization as a prime factor in the survival of Great Britain. Radar installations along the south coast of England detected the *Luftwaffe* in time for the R.A.F. fighter squadrons to become airborne and to intercept the bombers over the English Channel. The German radar was not very good, and they were desperate to improve their resolution. "Resolution" is the term for the ability of a lens (in the case of light) or an antenna to "see" sharply. Twenty/twenty vision means that your eyes have good resolving power, which is the ability to clearly separate two small objects at a distance — such as the letters on an eye chart.

The Germans wished to improve their radar antennas so that they could "see" small objects, such as distant fighter planes, clearly. In 1939, a German electrical engineer, Peter Mallach, discovered that at very short wavelengths in the centimeter region, dielectric substances made better antennas than did metal rods or bars. Glass is a dielectric substance, as are most plastics, including polystyrene rods, which can be used at centimeter (radar) wavelengths.

It is not necessary to go into the complexities of dielectric antennas other than to remember that they are in reality the opposite of metals, being made of an insulative material rather than a conductive material.

The waves transmitted, or collected, by a dielectric substance such as polystyrene, or other plastic, do not travel on the inside as do the waves in a metal radio waveguide, but rather on the surface of the rod or tube. For this reason, as in the case of mirrors at either end of a gas laser, they are called open resonator antennas, or "waveguides." In other words, they are capable of collecting (receiving) electromagnetic waves and guiding them to the detector in the receiver or, conversely, in the case of a transmitter, throwing waves out into the air in phase and marching together. A primary characteristic of all antenna design is that any substance that can be formed into a transmitting antenna can also be formed into a good receiving antenna. Thus, dielectric rods can efficiently transmit or receive.

Since the days of World War II, unfortunately, very little more research has been done on dielectric antennas. When I began to work in the late 1950s on measuring the dielectric properties of insect antennae, the papers on dielectric antennas could be listed on one page of a book.

Peter Mallach was captured after World War II and interrogated by the Air Force. It was his work that gave waveguide scientists a first good foothold on the characteristics of dielectric- (insulator-) type antenna waveguides. Even before Mallach, however, in 1933 G. C. Southworth, who then worked for the Bell Telephone

Laboratory, performed some experimental work on dielectric antennas.

It was the great British scientist, Lord Rayleigh (John William Strutt), who was the first person to suggest that a dielectric rod might be used to guide or collect electromagnetic waves. His paper, written in 1897, was entitled "On the Passage of Electric Waves Through Tubes." Lord Rayleigh was one of the great physical experimenters of all time. He contributed considerably to our knowledge of both sound and light waves, and is the father of the mathematics of resonance as applied to the physics of sound and light. His work on the resolving power of the optical lens is classical. He also developed the formula for finding the distribution of energy in a black body of long infrared wavelengths. Along with Herschel, who discovered these natural infrared rays, and Max Planck, who gave us the laws of radiation, he must be considered as a founder of the study of the infrared portion of the spectrum. Planck's laws explain how radiation is absorbed and emitted in "bundles" of energy that depend on the frequency of oscillations (vibrations) of the electrons of the atom.

In 1950, a graduate student, Chester M. McKinney, Jr., presented a dissertation entitled "Dielectric Wave Guides and Radiators" as a requirement for his Ph.D. degree at the University of Texas. This document may have been classified originally — I am not certain — as the work was performed for the Defense Research Laboratory at the University of Texas. At any rate, it was later distributed by the Clearinghouse for Federal Scientific and Technical Information of the Department of Commerce, by agreement with the Department of Defense. This is in keeping with the wise decision of the Federal government to declassify much of the work done at Defense Department laboratories. Significant findings from one laboratory, or area of study, may well apply in another field. Discoveries that are made by the financing of one scientific project, and that spill over into another research field, are called in today's jargon, "fallout." The fallout from NASA, for instance, was far more important to our country than the fact that a man walked on the moon. Almost everything I used in my laboratory at the USDA resulted from the fallout of our space effort. I need only add how much more satisfying it is to utilize fallout from discoveries resulting from a competition with another country in a race for the moon, than fallout from a race toward suicide-atomic war. Those who criticize our space effort do not realize that to accomplish that flight to the moon, a group of administrative geniuses, led by Wernher von Braun, put together, quite possibly, the greatest thinking organization in the history of the world. The organization was instructed to walk on the moon in ten years. They did as instructed in nine years. What a total lack of foresight was displayed when this magnificent organization was disbanded soon after the walk was finished. A single sentence from a farsighted leader would have kept those same brains working together. That sentence should have been, "Your mission is no longer to walk on the moon; rather, your mission is to solve the energy crisis and control all forms of pollution while doing so." Alas, such a mandate never came from our leaders.

When I received my copy of Dr. McKinney's dissertation from the Defense Documentations Center, I turned to page 154 where, in a special drawing, he showed the exact shape and measurements of the cylindrical dielectric rods that were used in his research. All of his rods and tubes were centimeters in length. They were designed to resonate at the short centimeter wavelengths. I was very excited to see that they looked exactly like the spines on an insect's antenna.

Another characteristic of their form was that they were tapered tubes. Engineers had found that by tapering their dielectric rods and tubes they could match the frequencies coming through the air to their dielectric tubes more efficiently. They obtained what electrical engineers call a good impedance (electrical resistance) match between the frequency traveling through the air, and the frequency traveling along the dielectric rod or tube to the receiver-detector. I also noted that their tapered dielectric rods were made out of polystyrene, Lucite, or wax filled with nujol — a well-known mineral oil.

A good dielectric (insulative) material, as distinguished from a good conductor, such as metal, has what is called a low dielectric constant. It is not necessary to explain the complexities of measuring the dielectric constant of a dielectric material. Years before I had read any of the reports on dielectric antennas, I had taken measurements of the insect exoskeleton (outer hard covering of insects). The best dielectric antennas have a low dielectric constant of approximately 2.5 to 6. The insect outer skeleton measured between 2.5 to 4. In other words, even though the insect is not made of metal, its outer covering, that is, the complex exoskeleton, is made of an excellent dielectric material. Furthermore, waxes (and especially beeswax) are excellent dielectrics. The outer exoskeleton of all insect spines is covered with a thin layer of wax only micrometers thin Another characteristic of a good dielectric antenna is that it should not only be tapered, but should also have thin walls.

Antenna engineers soon began discovering other things about dielectric waveguide antennas. For instance, by sculpturing the surface of their antennas they could make antenna configurations in which there was practically no electromagnetic loss of waves. Waves could be collected, or guided, with 100 percent efficiency to a receiver-detector. Researchers have found that surfaces could be helical (twisted), equiangular (twisted so that the spacing of the twist varies with the angle of twist), corrugated (ridged), terraced (step-like), and furrowed (V-shaped), as well as smooth. As wavelengths became shorter and shorter, design engineers were forced more and more to enter areas where the physics and mathematics of optics overlap with the physics and mathematics of microwave (radar) engineering.

Figure 11 is a drawing of the various types of spines on insect antennae that have been studied by me from the viewpoint of the antenna engineer. On the left are metal rod antennas that resonate in the microwave region of the radio spectrum. It soon became quite evident to me that the requirements for sculpturing of surface, tapering, thickness of wall, and form were all being met by the spine configurations that I saw on the insect antenna. Just as important, on one insect or another I found every single shape of antenna (scaled down to micrometers) that antenna engineers had designed to resonate at millimeter- or centimeter-long wavelengths. Many of these marvelous examples of micro-miniaturization of antennas can be seen in the plates of this book. They include such complex forms as sickle-shaped and loop antennas.

What we have been talking about all along is the beauty of form in nature. Birds and insects have the most intriguing forms. From early childhood, my primary interest in life had been the study of insects and birds. I was drawn to a study of insects in somewhat the same manner that I developed a love for birds. By the time I was twenty-one, the interrelationships of nature had become synthesized in my mind. I was developing from my reading an understanding of the connection existing between the flora

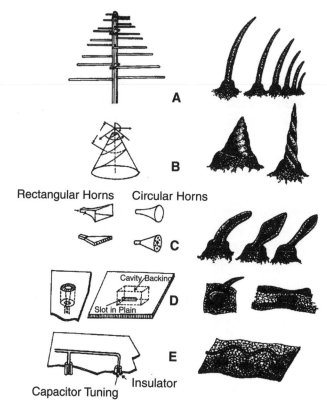

Rectangular Horns   Circular Horns

Cavity Backing

Slot in Plain

Capacitor Tuning   Insulator

Figure 11. Types of man-made electromagnetic antenna radiation collectors (*left*) and their insect dielectric counterparts (*right*).

A. Log-periodic array antenna. The elements, rods and spines of a log-periodic antenna are of shorter and shorter lengths, spaced on a log-periodic scale so that they slide from frequency to frequency across a wide band of frequencies. The cabbage looper and corn earworm moth *trichodea sensilla* (*right*) are arranged in this manner. In 1966 the author predicted these antenna function as log-periodic antennae. In 1974 he "tuned in" to the log-periodic infrared emissions from the cabbage looper sex scent called a pheromone.

B. Helical and equiangular spiral antenna. An equiangular spiral (*left and center*) is a single element log-periodic configuration. A conical type is found on the Florida scarab mite. Thin tapered helical-type dielectric sensilla are found on many species of wasps (*right*).

C. The "shoehorn" and "eared" furrowed configurations, called *auricillicum sensilla* on moths, have their counterparts in the horn configurations of microwave antennae.

D. Cavity and slot-type antenna waveguides are commonly used in the microwave region. Different types of dielectric cavities are common on the antennae of wasps and ants. The honey bee has dielectric pits on its antenna.

E. Many species of flies in the family *Cecidomyidae* have rings of loops called *circumfilla* on their antennae. Loop antennae are generally directional in nature. This plate shows only a few of the antenna configurations developed by man, the dielectric counterparts of which are found on insects.

and fauna of the countryside. Ecology, the study of the relationship of living things to their total environment, was a rapidly growing branch of biology. I had already decided during World War II that when I returned to college I would become an ecologist, but I still thought my main interest lay in the study of bird life.

I knew about the effects of weather on life, but I wished to delve into this topic more thoroughly. In 1945, Ellsworth Huntington published his *Mainsprings of Civilization*, a penetrating analysis of how climate, weather, diet, geography, and heredity control the character of an entire nation and help to shape its history. His chapter on cycles and rhythms was fascinating, and later, as I traveled around the world, I observed with startling regularity the truth of many of his deductions about the development of human civilizations.

One of the greatest mysteries in the study of biology is, of course, sex. It may be determined, for example, that one moth attracts another by a special scent given off, or that the attraction is instinctive, whatever that means, for instinct is a word the biologist often uses when no other explanation is available. The discovery of a sexual behavioral pattern based on scent, color, sound, shape, or other physical parameters, does not in and of itself explain what has happened. Why, for instance, is the scent or color so attractive? How does it work on the nervous system to create attraction? Attractant is a word that entomologists like to use in labeling their insect scents. But why do the scents attract? Why do they stimulate? Do insects and birds have emotions — perhaps to a lesser degree than humans? Analyzing sex attraction in the human is an almost impossible task. The human male is stimulated by the shapely — and especially the nude — female form. This stimulant is universal, but the fact that there exists a sexual stimulant at the highest of rational levels doesn't explain how it works, and does not give one any knowledge of human love at all. Love is one of the most written about of our emotions, but it is totally unexplainable to the human mind (the intellect). Perhaps because love is an emotion of the mind as well as the intellect, and because the mind as the instrument of study is attempting to explain itself, no explanation would be possible.

The Japanese treat the human form much more naturally than do Westerners. Often at the village bathhouse, with my fishermen

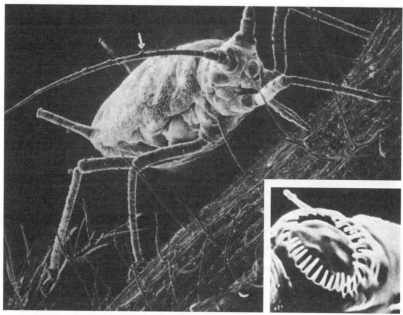

A tiny green peach aphid on a Desmodium stem. Plants are covered with microscopic hairs called trichomes (*Chapter 12*). The white arrow points to the round, dome-shaped sensor on the antenna (shown enlarged a thousand times in the insert). The dome-shaped sensor is surrounded by curved spines, and illustrates an array antenna configuration. Dome-shaped sensors on insects are generally called *Placodea sensilla*. Placodea sensilla represent the reduced extreme of a spine — a long spine that has been widened and flattened until it becomes like a lens-antenna instead of a spine-type antenna.

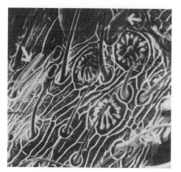

Sensory sensilla on the antenna of the red-banded leaf roller moth. The long tapered *trichodea* (spine) and *coeloconica* (picket fence) sensilla are present on all night-flying moths. The picket fence sensor is more open than that of the cabbage looper moth. The trichodea sensilla are arranged further apart than the trichodea on the cabbage looper moth antenna. Infrared frequencies detected by any one moth species will depend on the arrangement (array), length and diameter of the sensilla. The right arrow points to an "eared" and the left arrow to a "shoe-horned" sensilla. They were first described by the author and are called *auricillicum* sensilla. They have a furrowed configuration. The furrow is pitted with small apertures. I believe these are host plant scent sensors, but have no proof. Such furrowed antenna configurations are usually associated with "shaped" field patterns of electromagnetic radiation like figure-eight patterns, etc.

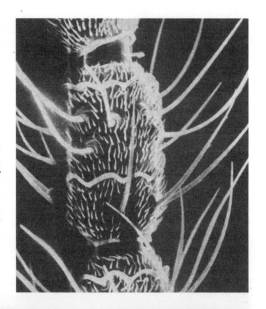

Long trichodea sensilla and loop sensilla on the antenna of a species of gall midge (*Diptera: Cecidomyidae*). The loops circle the antenna segment and are called *circumfilla* sensilla. Loop configurations are usually directional. Circumfilla of different heights and arrangements occur on the antenna of most gall midges. The Hessian fly that destroys wheat in the Midwest belongs to the gall midge family.

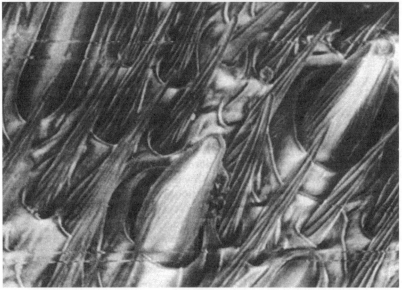

Pyramidal and corrugated helical sensilla on the antenna of *Polistes metricus*, a species of paper wasp. Helical antenna may be considered a special form of loop antenna and are highly directional. If the helix is in the form of an equiangular spiral, it may also be a broadband (log-periodic) antenna and resonate to more than one frequency. Antenna elements (sensilla) can also be arranged as different lengths in a log-periodic fashion from the base to the tip, and thus form an array log-periodic antenna (*Chapter 10*) which resonates to a series of log-periodic emitted frequencies.

friends in Japan, there were young mothers present sitting in the hot pool of water, their children clasped to their breasts. I wondered how the Westerner has managed to distort human biology so that such a vision of unclad tender motherhood is considered vulgar. Perhaps the Japanese, able to mix with passionless detachment the bathing families of a little village, are a people who have arrived at a truer understanding of creation. In their love of detail, of form, and of the transient things of life, they seem to incorporate into their being a spiritual universality with all creation.

There are Ama (sea women) villages in many areas along the Japanese coast. Diving for pearls is not the Ama divers real trade, as is believed by most Americans. In coastal villages these graceful fishing girls dive for awabi, a delicious shell food, or sea plants such as kelp.

Not far from Chiba at the head of Bosa peninsula (called the "Kitchen of Tokyo" because its seafood, fruits, and vegetables feed that great city), I often stopped at an Ama village to watch the seafood-gathering girls rising from the sea to dry themselves by beach fires. I discovered these secluded diving beaches while looking for Japanese black-winged stilts and oystercatchers along the Boso coastline. I was young enough to sit and stare in wonder at the misty vision of human bodies and huge Asiatic gulls clamoring for bits from the Ama catch.

The human form is surrounded by an infrared aurora, as is the night-flying moth. Of course we do not "modulate" that radiation with flapping wings, but perhaps the sea gulls do this with their wings. Who knows? The subtle molecular body scents, or other body gases that surround our bodies, are radiated by our own black body infrared emission which glows in the 10-micrometer window like a steady-glowing infrared light bulb. Could the CO_2, the molecules of lactic acid from our muscular actions, or even unknown sex scents drifting from our bodies, be stimulated to emit narrowband fluorescent infrared colors? Are our body odors stimulated to emit by our own broadband black body radiation, and thus fluoresce narrowband infrared frequencies that are attractive to mosquitoes, deer flies, biting flies — or, for that matter, even subconsciously through sex scents to our own mates? Maybe the young are closer to the truth than we are willing to admit when they say that two people who really like each other have vibrations, or "vibes," between them.

For fifteen years I plotted the distribution and arrangement of the spines on the corn earworm moth antenna. Entomologists call these microminiature sensory spines sensilla. Electro physiological nerve studies (detection of nerve impulses by electronic means) had already shown that these sensilla sensors respond to odor molecules.

With a light microscope it was extremely difficult to really see the shape of the little antenna sensilla. Most of them measured between two and 150 micrometers in length and had a diameter of less than three micrometers at the base. One furrowed type that I named the "shoehorn sensillum," was very uncommon on the antenna. My excellent technician, Thelma Carlysle, had to make more than 1,000 slides before we finally decided what it really looked like. The technique is to embed the antenna in paraffin; then to cut the block of paraffin into micro-thin slices. Each slice is observed under the microscope, and the image of the sensillum built up by putting the layers back together like slices of a loaf of bread. Since the image can be reconstructed only in the mind, one must have a three-dimensional brain to reconstruct the form. This is apparently a talent that artists and morphologists are born with.

About the time I published the first complete morphology of a noctuid moth antenna, the scanning electron microscope was invented by a group of physicists working at Cambridge University in England.

One of the first scanning scopes put together in this country was installed under the direction of Dr. Charles Susskind at the University of California Electronic Research Center. I immediately flew to California with some corn earworm moths, and we looked at the antenna under this marvelous new microscope. Paul Griffith, a graduate student at the Electronic Research Center, completed the job in less than two weeks. It gave me a great deal of satisfaction to note that none of my descriptions of the corn earworm antenna needed correcting. All nine types of antenna sensilla that it took me fifteen years to describe showed up in exact detail in the photographs from the scanning scope. I knew I had to get my own instrument, and when I did was both excited and disheartened over the fact that what it took me fifteen years to accomplish previously could now be completed in fifteen days. Alas, such is scientific progress.

For years I had studied Dr. McKinney's thesis on dielectric waveguides and radiators. I have always wondered about the thinking of the individuals in the Defense Department who make up code names. I never paid much attention to the code name of my unclassified document, but one day the fine print at the top of a page caught my eye. Had some Defense Department scientific administrator been watching closely the insects in his garden? The code name given to Dr. McKinney's research report was *Bumblebee Report No. 138!*

The Wondrous World of Wax

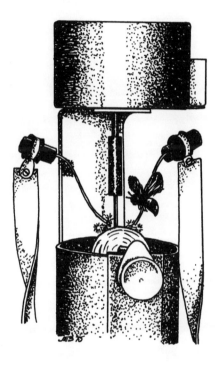

Chapter 7

The Wondrous World of Wax

The external body covering of living organisms is called the integument, from the Latin word meaning "to cover." The integument of the insect is a specialized type of outer covering sometimes referred to as the exoskeleton. Since insects have no framework of bones, the exoskeleton is really an outside skeleton, as the name suggests. It is constructed of an extremely hard substance. This hard external skeleton determines the shape of the insect and is released in a fluid state by the inner epithelium — the innermost tissue beneath the insect's hard body wall. Once set, it forms hard, rigid plates called sclerites. The sclerites are separated from each other by membranes that allow a certain amount of flexibility between them. The very outermost layer of the exoskeleton is called the epicuticle or outer cuticle. The insect antenna sensillae are tubular extensions of this outer cuticle.

During the process of formation of the cuticle, two unique substances are secreted from the inner epithelium cells through small pore canals that lead to the surface. One of the substances is a shellac-like liquid that hardens into the outermost layer, called the cement layer. Just below the cement layer are two layers of wax. The innermost layer of wax is made up of wax molecules lined up like rows of upright bricks so that they form what is called a monolayer, or single *orientated wax layer*. Just above the wax layer, between it and the outer cement layer, is a thicker layer of *randomly orientated wax molecules*. We see then that the very outermost covering of the insect exoskeleton consists of two extremely thin layers of wax covered with an even thinner layer of shellac-like cement.

Water evaporates from an organism at a rate that depends on the amount of its surface area, not on the volume of the animal. As size decreases, the ratio of surface-to-volume increases; thus, small insects lose relatively more water than do larger ones in a given time. Such insects face the necessity of keeping the small bit of water in their bodies from evaporating. It is the epicuticle, and especially the outer waxy layers, that prevent excessive drying out of their bodies.

Because it controls water balance, the integument is one of the most important organs for fitting the insect to its environment. It also performs another important function: it is the substrate or basic surface that supports all of the sensory sensilla (also the eyes) that form the insect's communication system. It is the eyes and, just as important, the sensilla sensors that allow the insect to find its way around in its environment. Since the sensory sensilla are an integral part of the exoskeleton, they are also covered by the waxy-cement epicuticle.

Entomologists have long known that the epicuticle controls water balance in the insect, but they have totally overlooked another very important property of insect wax: its electret properties.

An electret substance may be thought of as analogous to a magnet. It has fixed opposite charges on opposite surfaces. Just as a magnet is a material with a magnetic field at its opposite poles, an electret is a material with an electric field on its opposite surfaces. Like a magnet, an electret is a static system, not a source of current as is a battery. The charge on each surface is fixed, like the plus and minus poles of a magnet. Because of the stability of the opposite poles, it was called an electret — a word like magnet that ends in "et". Substances passing near an electret — molecules for instance — or touching an electret will affect the static potential difference on an electret. It has been known for some 30 years that electrets can be used to "catch" pollution molecules out of the air, just as a magnet can "catch" metal particles.

Electrets were discovered in 1733 by Stephen Gray, and rediscovered in 1922 by a Japanese physicist, Dr. Mototaro Eguchi. In his early experiments, Eguchi produced electrets by solidifying mixtures of a plant wax, called carnauba wax (from palm trees), and beeswax in a constant electric field. Eguchi's electrets were later called thermoelectrets because it was discovered that they formed by the simultaneous action of the heat (IR) and an electric field. It was later shown that they could be produced without melting and solidification at all, simply by cooling a solid dielectric, such as beeswax, in an electric field. This is especially easy to do with a very thin-layer electret of a wax. Physicists showed that the best thermoelectrets were certain polycrystalline waxes, such as beeswax, plant waxes, various hydrocarbons and alcohols.

The electrical conductivity (ability to conduct current) of thermoelectrets can be increased or decreased by irradiation with certain wavelengths of the electromagnetic spectrum. Physicists have shown also that the thermoelectret charge depends upon the humidity of the air. Storage of a thermoelectret in excessive humidity will produce a sharp fall in charge and high humidity may wipe out the long-lived charge completely. At this point it may be well to mention that insects do not function well in either extremely high, or extremely low, humidity, e.g., the optimum relative humidity for the corn earworm moth is 40 to 70 percent as I showed by experimentation as early as 1955.

Some of Dr. Eguchi's original electrets made fifty years ago, and kept short-circuited between metal plates, still have about 20 percent of their electrical charge left. The permanence of an electret substance is obvious from Dr. Eguchi's original shorted electrets.

Thermoelectrets exhibit some rather strange properties. One is that if an electret with a plus charge on one surface, and a minus charge on the other, is cut in half, two electrets with similar charges will be formed. Another characteristic is that if the two opposite sides of an electret are kept shorted, the charge will last for years, but if the electret is left out to be influenced by some environmental factor, it may slowly lose its charge, or even more mysteriously switch charges on each of its surfaces. Melting a thermoelectret destroys its properties. Researchers have prepared stable thermoelectrets from plant waxes, Pyrex glass, sugar, beeswax, sulphur, Lucite, nylon and plastics of various types. All of these substances have low dielectric constants, and thus can be considered as having the solid-state electrical properties suitable for forming waveguide antennas.

Researchers soon discovered that the formation of the complex charges on electrets was intimately related to the environment. In other words, the charges are affected by temperature, humidity, pressure, and especially by irradiation by various electromagnetic wavelengths. To sum it up in a nutshell, the insect sensillum is not only an excellent dielectric waveguide, but is covered with insect wax which itself contains all the physical properties for detecting absolutely any environmental factor surrounding the insect. Not only can thermoelectrets be utilized to regulate energy of different types, but since certain environmental factors cause the opposite surface charges to switch from one surface to the other, or even to trickle off with time, they can be used as switching mechanisms, or time constant memory circuits.

The capabilities of electrets for electronic control and detecting systems is limitless. In spite of the fact they were rediscovered in 1922, they have just lately been utilized by solid-state designers in modern electronic circuits. As I pointed out before, electrets are sensitive to pressure. Sound waves are pressure waves in the air.

Considerable progress was made in the early '70s in utilizing manmade plastic electrets. At that time, it was estimated that there were more than eight million electret microphones produced each year by multinational companies involved in solid-state manufacturing of electronic components.

What I have said up to now is fact, but the real fun of science is theorizing, and then testing the theories to see if they hold water, or if they should be discarded for more likely theories. Dr. E. R. Laithwaite, an electrical engineer at Imperial University in London, has a hobby of collecting butterflies and moths. He believes, as I do, that the moth antenna resembles to a striking degree a real radar antenna. In 1960 he wrote a paper entitled "A Radiation Theory of the Assembling of Moths."

Dr. Laithwaite had noticed a moth species, called in England "the Vapourer," flying with the wind to a female. Since scent would have to float downwind towards a male, for the male flying against the wind to find the emitting scent, he decided there must be an electromagnetic signal which could go out in any direction, irregardless of wind. Later we will see why Dr. Laithwaite was both correct and incorrect in his assumption.

In 1964, the year I hiked across the Dartmoor after the international meeting of entomologists in London, I was involved in the best example I have ever experienced of scientists being so narrow that they were unable to see one another's points of view. There were three researchers involved, and none of the three was listening to the other — once again an example of scientists as their own worst enemies.

Dr. Laithwaite, a brilliant electrical engineer, was working on an antigravity system. Dr. H. B. D. Kettlewell, an eminent entomologist, is the earliest researcher in the area of insect sex scents that today we call pheromones. In fact it was really Kettlewell who first showed that moths find each other by scent. Kettlewell coined the phrase "assembling" for the attraction of moths and butterflies to one another. Since he was certain that "assembling," as he called it, involved scent, and Laithwaite was certain that it was electromagnetic infrared radiation given off by the moth's body, the two men engaged in a knock-down-drag-out professional battle as to who knew most about what. The subject is entomological in nature, so Dr. Laithwaite was considered an upstart and an outsider fighting a losing battle. All the entomologists knew Kettlewell was right, because they had not long before succeeded in isolating sex scents from the Gypsy moth, and also from a large species of *saturniid* moth.

The third researcher was Dr. R. H. Wright. Dr. Wright, a physical chemist, had been working on mammalian smell, and believed that perhaps insects and mammals decoded odor (he has never said how) by identifying what is called osmic frequencies from odor molecules. Osmic frequencies are absorption bands caused by the intermolecular vibrations of molecules. The absorption frequencies occur mostly in the far-infrared portion of the spectrum.

What we have, in essence, is an entomologist saying that the insect antenna detects scent; an electrical engineer saying that the insect antenna detects infrared radiation, and a physical chemist saying that it detects infrared radiation *from* scent. I was in the middle trying to explain that in all probability each one was correct and that we should get together and work the different theories out. Since I had a broad view of electronics, entomology, physics and physical chemistry (I had started reading texts on the latter subject), I was sure we could set up some experiments to get the three scientific approaches into one box. Laithwaite was the most open minded, but he was in Manchester and, besides, Kettlewell wasn't talking to him. I tried to explain to Dr. Wright that probably all three were right, but he was so absorbed in correlating infrared absorption bands that he was not interested in my dielectric antenna theories. Nor was Kettlewell interested.

Insect physiologists had little use for either Laithwaite's or my theory that the insect antenna really is an electromagnetic antenna; it didn't fit their chemical views.

Since none of these three researchers was interested in talking to the other, I decided that I would probably end up doing all of the experimenting myself. I departed for the Dartmoor, and when I arrived back in my lab in Tifton, Georgia, I bought a shelfful of laser physics books. It was unfortunate that in 1964 there was no real way to tune into certain infrared frequencies — especially narrowband frequencies — but I was completely convinced that Laithwaite, Kettlewell and Wright were all at least partly correct and that the real answer lay in looking for infrared emission frequencies, not absorption osmic frequencies, as Wright was doing. I decided that these postulated frequencies from the scent molecules were probably narrowband and quite strong even though we couldn't detect them. I named them maser-like frequencies for their presumed characteristics of being narrowband and high energy — at least high energy — in the far-infrared part of the spectrum where, in terms of electron volts, the energy is very low. Maser-like in my mind meant molecular or, better yet, *M*icrometer *A*mplification by *S*timulated *E*mission of *R*adiation.

Lasers (*L*ight *A*mplification by *S*timulated *E*mission of *R*adiation) had been theorized and invented by Townes and his colleagues in 1954-55. I had been following the physics of laser development very closely. Every year I went to Kessler Field on active duty as a communications officer, and between duties as a squadron commander; I read everything I could about lasers. Townes had done his work at Columbia University under an Air Force grant, but again, the Air Force had decided very wisely not to classify the work. It wouldn't have done any good if they had classified it, for two Russians, N. G. Bosov and A. M. Prokhorov, invented the laser at exactly the same time that Towne did. In 1965, all three of these researchers received the Nobel Prize for their work. The invention of the laser illustrates the futility of classifying scientific discoveries as top secret. It never really works because too many scientific minds are thinking in the same way, at the same time, in different parts of the world.

If the entomologists at the London meeting didn't think much of my infrared antenna theories, at least one science reporter did. An English friend later sent me a clipping from a British scientific magazine. I read it with some amusement, for apparently I had said too much too fast.

Insects "Tuned In" To Infrared Rays

The fact that certain kinds of moths can attract a mate over a distance of a mile or two in the dark was established by the great French naturalist, Jean-Henri Fabre, in the middle of the 19th Century. Since then entomologists have been trying to find out how they do it. Various theories have been put forward. One is that female moths emit sexual scents — but in some cases there is the snag that some of them seem to be able to emit them up wind.

At the International Entomological Congress in London last week, Dr. Philip S. Callahan, an American who has put in a lot of work on the infamous fire ant, advanced the novel explanation that the attraction can take the form of electromagnetic radiation — in particular, rays at the long-wave end of the infrared. In a week which produced a lot of new information about insects, this was perhaps the most surprising item of all.

Although Dr. Callahan's paper was somewhat blurred by the speed at which he had given his paper (as one delegate put it, it was like listening to the history of the second World War in five minutes), certain facts emerged clearly enough. . . .

The rest of the article went on to give a fairly straightforward review of my theories of insect communication.

In 1964, I started to work to test the response of different moth species to far-infrared radiation. At that time only a very few narrowband infrared frequencies had been produced by lasers. None of the wavelengths "fitted" the length of the antennae sensilla on the corn earworm, cabbage looper or fall armyworm noctuid species that we reared in our laboratory.

A laboratory in Michigan had reported that the corn earworm moth was attracted to a cyanide laser. The cyanide laser emits a strong infrared line, 337 micrometers long. I was elated because it was fairly good evidence that noctuid moths were "tuning in" to the narrowband far-infrared frequencies. Although I was elated, I was also puzzled, for all of my waveguide antenna mathematics indicated that the sensilla were open waveguide resonators. As mentioned in Chapter 6, open resonators are waveguides, or antennas on whose surfaces the waves travel, and, of course, these antennas should be more than one wavelength long. The longest sensilla on the corn earworm antenna were 46 micrometers long, and 46 into 337 micrometer wavelength gives an antenna sensillum approximately $\frac{1}{7}$ wavelength long. In the radio region we use $\frac{1}{4}$- and $\frac{1}{2}$-long wavelength antennas, but I never heard of a $\frac{1}{7}$ wavelength antenna. In fact, for an open resonator, McKinney's work indicated that the antenna sensilla ought to be at least 2 to 6 wavelengths long, not $\frac{1}{7}$ of the wavelength.

With the aid of Edsel Harold, an engineer in our lab, I immediately set to work in constructing what I later referred to as my RIM (Russian Infrared Machine). Some of my friends called it IRM (Idiot's Russian Machine). In 1924, Dr. Glagolewa-Arkadiewa generated and detected long-wave far-infrared frequencies with this machine, which she designed while working at the Moscow magnetic lab. She was the first researcher to close the spectrum between the near-infrared wavelengths (0.8 to 3 micrometers) and the far-infrared (out to 1,000 micrometers), or one millimeter (mm) where microwave begins (see *Figure 1*) The machine was ingenious and simple, as have been many really elegant experiments.

Dr. Arkadiewa suspended minute metal filings in mineral oil, and rotated a wheel through the metal-filled oil mixture so that the particles went around on the edge of the wheel like a tire on a car wheel. She put a high voltage arc across the edge of the wheel. Her assumption was that the strong electric discharge would cause the minute metal filings to oscillate at extremely short wavelengths. Her hypothesis was correct as she succeeded in detecting wavelengths from 80 to approximately 500 micrometers long. She was the first researcher to close the electromagnetic gap — and a big gap it was — between the near-infrared and the millimeter-microwave portion of the spectrum. This single experiment was worthy of a Nobel Prize, but sadly enough she never received one.

When I put my moths in front of the Russian IR Machine, they did everything from trying to lay eggs on it, to various male species trying to mate with the wheel by reaching their male genitalia toward it. Wasps and bees orientated their antennae toward it. Again I was elated, and decided that the Michigan researchers were correct — that the sensilla were $\frac{1}{7}$-long dielectric waveguides.

This experiment confirmed that the insect antenna had electret properties. Whenever I placed an isolated moth antenna in the alternating AC field (60 cycles), it vibrated back and forth like a vibrating reed, at 60 cycles. Although I grounded the antenna, it still continued to vibrate in the AC field, indicating that it had a stable (thermoelectret) charge permanently fixed to it.

Since the Russian IR machine put out many, many frequencies, like a "shotgun," mainly between 80 and 1,000 micrometers, and some very strong ones between 300 and 343 micrometers, I felt that it demonstrated that the Michigan group was correct, despite my waveguide mathematics. Not only had I shown that the insect antenna was an electret with my machine, but I had decided that I might be able to filter out all but the 300- to 343-micrometer frequencies, and use the machine instead of an expensive $18,000 cyanide laser to study the attraction to the 339-micrometer frequency. I still could not understand why the dielectric sensilla spines on the antenna resonated way out at 337 micrometers. Another thing that I noticed about my "shotgun" emitter, however, was that the moth's behavior in the presence of the turning wheel often resembled a moth's suicidal behavior at a candle flame. This convinced me even further that both the Russian IR machine and a candle flame emitted a lot of different, unknown far-IR frequencies.

In the back of my mind I still suspected that the Russian IR machine must also put out 2- to 30-micrometer frequencies, even though Dr. Glagolewa-Arkadiewa's spectrum showed none.

In 1969, I transferred to the new USDA Insect Attractants Lab on the campus of the University of Florida at Gainesville. Dr. Ken Turner, an agricultural engineer, also transferred, from Iowa State to Gainesville. I accepted his invitation to fly out to the Bureau of Standards Laboratory at Boulder, Colorado, and to repeat the Michigan experiments, utilizing the bureau's cyanide laser. I returned to Gainesville, more convinced than ever that I should stick to my own dielectric waveguide theory and search in the 2- to 30- or 40-micrometer region. We never succeeded in repeating the Michigan experiments, and I believe to this day that those researchers were fooled by stray UV black light coming from the laser tube. You will remember, as I pointed out in Chapter 2, that many species of insects are attracted to black light because the compound eye is capable of detecting near UV in the black light range.

I had been led astray by the well-meaning physicists who did not really understand the behavior of night-flying moths. Had they bothered to check with me before writing up their experiments, I might have prevented the misinformation from going out. What the cyanide-laser experiment illustrated is the danger of being a generalist and cutting across fields. As I pointed out in the introduction, the handholds are not well known and one constantly risks making horrible mistakes. My friends at the infrared lab in Michigan were excellent physicists and their experiments appeared to be well planned, but they just didn't know enough about the life of a moth.

In the new lab in Gainesville, I traversed the cliff side from the handholds that were leading to nowhere at 337 micrometers and again attained my own route up the craggy rocks of science toward the 2- to 30-micrometer part of the spectrum. I could see the candlelight flickering at the top of the mountain, for I had more faith in the dielectric antenna waveguide theory than I had in the experiments of the physicists. I believe God is a better design engineer than are engineers or scientists.

I decided I needed a further check on my idea that the insect exoskeleton is a wax-coated thermoelectret. With the help of my technician, Thelma Carlysle, I cut off some corn earworm moth and cabbage looper antennae and immersed them in a neutral liquid mounting media called CMC-10. Measurements on the antenna indicated it had a total plus charge. We dropped a few grains of a negatively charged dye called aniline blue into the mounting media and, sure enough, as we watched through the microscope the small particles of dye moved slowly toward the sensilla spines of the antenna. Within one half hour the sensilla were lined with a coating of the dye which moved steadily along to the spot on each sensillum where there are small apertures in the tip, or sides, of this gracefully curved rod. I knew as I watched that a moth fly-

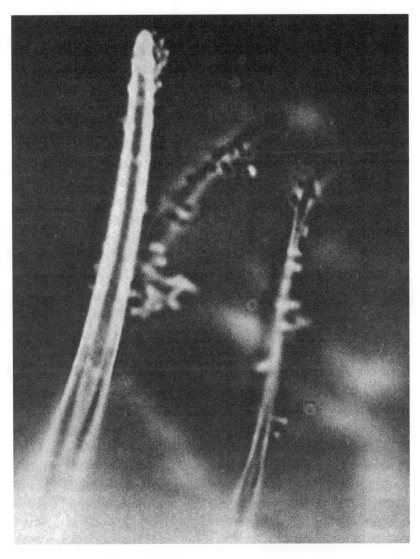

Negatively charged particles of the dye crystal violet attracted to the sensilla of the cabbage looper moth. The large sensilla is a *chaetica* type and the dye is attracted to the tip where a single pore is located. The sensilla in the background are curved *trichodea* types and the dye is attracted to the sides of the curved portion where numerous pores are located. Since the sensilla have a positive electret charge, they collect molecules from the air by their fixed attractive charge, proving them to have thermoelectret properties.

ing through the air attracts wind-carried molecules to its surface. It was not surprising to me, for the antenna-thermoelectret properties assured that the free-floating molecules would be pulled to the delicate microscopic sensilla. I performed these experiments in 1965. By 1975, physicists were using plastic thermoelectrets to attract pollution molecules from the dirty air over cities. The molecules being studied in this manner included alcohols, acetates and aldehydes. These are the very same types of molecules that constitute most sex and host-plant insect attractants.

The Candle Mystery

Chapter 8
The Candle Mystery

Why does a moth seek self-destruction in the flickering flame of a candle? This curious behavior of moths has intrigued me since early boyhood when I first read French entomologist J. Henri Fabre's speculations on the phenomenon. In a strange and beautiful essay called "The Great Peacock Moth," he described the wild rush of the large moth to a candle. One might liken it to a desire of the moth to "kill" the flickering fire because it competed with the natural moon and starlight. Thomas Carlyle, the renowned English poet, attributed the moth's behavior to passionate love.

Tragedy of the Night-Moth
Magna ausus

'Tis placid midnight, stars are keeping
    Their meek and silent course in heaven;
Save pale recluse, for knowledge seeking,
    All mortal things to sleep are given.

But see! a wandering Night-moth enters,
    Allured by taper gleaming bright;
Awhile keeps hovering round, then ventures
    On Goethe's mystic page to light,

With awe she views the candle blazing;
    A universe of fire it seems
To moth-savante with rapture gazing,
    Or Fount whence Life and Motion streams.

What passion in her small heart whirling,
Hopes boundless, adoration, dread;
At length her tiny pinions twirling,
She darts, and — puff ! — the moth is dead.

The sullen flame, for her scarce sparkling,
Gives but one hiss, one fitful glare;
Now bright and busy, now all darkling,
She snaps and fades to empty air.

Her bright grey form that spread so slimly,
Some fan she seemed of pygmy Queen;
Her silky cloak that lay so trimly,
Her wee, wee eyes that looked so keen.

Last moment, here, now gone forever,
To naught are passed with fiery pain;
And ages circling round shall never
Give to this creature shape again!

Poor moth! thy fate my own resembles.
Me, too, a restless, asking mind
Hath sent on far and weary rambles,
To seek the good I ne'er shall find.

Like thee, with common lot contented,
With humble joys and vulgar fate,
I might have lived and ne'er lamented,
Moth of a larger size, a longer day!

But Nature's majesty unveiling
What seemed her wildest, grandest charms,
Eternal Truth and Beauty hailing,
Like thee, I rushed into her arms.

What gained we, little moth? Thy ashes,
Thy one brief parting pang may show:
And thoughts like these, for soul that dashes
From deep to deep, are death more slow!

In this lucid and beautiful poetic outpouring, Thomas Carlyle was closer to truth than the world would suspect. The poem is a fairly accurate description of a moth's behavior at a candle flame.

I can remember one night of candle-moth watching. At age twenty-four, I quit my job in Japan to hike around the world. On that trip I carried a large candle in my rucksack. When I reached the Middle East, I hiked north up the Euphrates River and crossed the Syrian desert to the edge of the Mediterranean. From there I took a boat to the Italian city of Bari, and from Bari I hiked north across the Murgie hills in the province of Apulia. Night overtook me before I reached my destination, the Castle del Monte. The octagon-shaped castle is also called the Crown of Apulia because it perches on an isolated hilltop. The "crown" was the ancient hunting lodge of the great scientist and emperor, Frederick II of Hohenstaufen. It was at the Crown of Apulia that he housed and trained his hunting falcons.

I had thrown my rucksack to the ground under a thick, rounded evergreen tree near the road. The night air was crisp, but not cold, and a soft winter rain had greened the fresh shoots of grass sticking up from the crunchy Italian soil. I lit the big wax candle taken from the pocket of my rucksack and dated the top of a page in my journal. It was a relief to be out of the hot Middle Eastern desert and hiking in the stimulating air that flowed from the Adriatic Sea.

I was awakened from my recollections of the desert Bedouins I was writing about by a small brown moth that flew from the grass and began making darting passes at the flickering point of candle-light. I forgot my writing to observe the night creature. It was one of those moths that in warmer climates emerges from the shelter of the ground ahead of schedule and perishes from lack of nectar, since the flowering of plants is not upon the land. Perhaps an especially warm day, following a little cold, tricks them from the shelter of the protective Earth, and they emerge from their pupal case out of synchronization with the great rhythm of nature. In America, farmers call all such little brown moths "miller moths," for some species are to be found in their stored grain bins.

This moth would not starve, for it sought release from its fate in the heat of the flame. First it singed each of its wings, then returned for a third successful dive and plunged into the candle. Wax and protoplasm and the hard shell sizzled and burned for a second, and a little spiral of smoke ascended from the waxy crematorium drifting upward among the needled boughs of the evergreen.

Why, I thought to myself, do you, little moth, seek your death? At the time, I had observed one of nature's greatest mysteries that memorable evening, but no entomologist, no scientist had yet answered this baffling mystery. Did the Emperor Frederick II take any notice of insects? The writings of this eminent naturalist do not indicate any thoughts of, or interest in, insects. Why do many species of night-flying moths plunge into the fire of a lighted candle? They will not be so attracted by the same-colored flame of a burning piece of wood. Why do they not fly into one's campfire? If the great attraction were visible light, then surely both types of flame would be equally attractive. Both appear to flicker with the same hues of blue, green, and yellow to the human eye. Perhaps the little brown moth actually was in love with the flickering light. If so, there must be something besides visible light glowing from the hot, wax candle flame. I remembered what I had learned from chemistry of flame spectroscopy, and how the instructor had described the many other frequencies in the ultraviolet and infrared wavelengths that were emitted from such flames. The candle was, after all, partially beeswax, a substance made from insects; perhaps such petroleum and wax products made of carbon, hydrogen, and oxygen atoms duplicated some unknown frequency that the moth could sense, but we could not. Perhaps there were infrared or other electronic signals coming from that heated flame that we could not even imagine, but were signals that aroused the passions of mothdom to an ecstasy of boundless adoration — as Carlyle wrote — a sort of love siren luring the passionate lover to his death.

How many nights had Frederick II worked on his manuscript by a flickering taper in his great marble-walled audience chamber, and been interrupted by some medieval moth darting back and forth in his light? Had he been angry, or had he stopped to speculate on the strange, self-destructive behavior of the moth? Probably the latter, for he was as much a scientist as he was an emperor. Yet, there were no screens on the high castle windows, so perhaps he became annoyed at such constant disrespect for the royal person. Perhaps on a starlit night he would take one of his favorite birds on his fist and, in the refreshing evening air that flowed over the Terra Di Bari from the sea, cool his anger with visions of the next morning's hunt over the downs that stretched to the horizon around the great castle.

That next morning, so many years ago, I awoke from my soft, Earthy bed to a falconer's dawn. The red ball of the sun hung in the east, hardly peeking over the grove of olive trees that lined the horizon. I slung my rucksack over my shoulders and started the climb up the gradual rise of the Terra Di Bari to the Murgie down. From the scrub along the road came a loud "tyi-uc-tyi-uc" — a tawny pipit strutted into the road and, seeing the early morning hiker, flew off into the scantily covered heath. Against the darker western sky, a lone heron flapped slowly along heading for one of the little creeks that drops to the Adriatic, but is seldom seen as it lies concealed between the undulating hills of the downs. It was indeed a falconer's day, and I was under the same spell, dallying along, using every excuse to stop and view the scenery, or to attempt to identify some new bird. I did not care that I had no traveling companion, for the resurrection of such a dawn is best suited to the lone traveler, and any human intrusion into my meditative thoughts would have broken the spell. I understand why Christ liked the image of the shepherd — a lonely wanderer among the rolling hills, sitting at dawn by his breakfast fire, the whole Earth and sky a cathedral. Thoughts of love and peace come easily at such times and in such a place — far more easily than in the grandeur of man's most beautiful cathedrals.

Memories of that night in the Murgie hills, and also of those nights at the outpost radio station in Ireland stuck in my mind, imprinted there like stored "bits" in my memory bank. I was not the first to believe that perhaps insects sense radiation from oscillating molecules. From the early eighteenth century, many naturalists have considered the possibility that insects communicate by some sort of private radio system.

That mysterious system has been called many things by many people (see Table 2), and is recorded in the writings of these gentlemen, who were not necessarily entomologists by profession, although all were students of nature.

Entomological literature contains a vast amount of speculation concerning a nebulous sixth sense that insects appear to possess. A certain few field observers have been unable to attribute to scent alone the fantastic ability of insects to find specific mates and hosts among the myriads of nature's species. This does not mean that scent does not play an important role, but only that some other subtle factor is equally as important. A common thread runs

The beautiful white-lined sphinx moth in flight. A tiger moth rests on the infrared light sensor on the left. The white-lined sphinx is my favorite species of moth. This species is attracted to fluorescent lights and candle flames. It often flies in daylight as well as at night. Note how stable the two antennae are in flight.

Black lubber grasshopper. This large southern grasshopper has poorly developed wings, and is flightless. It is a southern species that is attracted to and feeds on numerous roadside plants. Note that the insect antenna is segmented like beads on a string. Each segment has hundreds of the microminiature sensilla that are utilized for detecting the host plant and sex scents (called sex pheromones or more generally kairomones).

Female wolf spider with egg sack. The handsome wolf spiders hunt at night and stalk their prey by pouncing upon the victim with great vigor. The female wolf spider is a solicitous mother and encloses her eggs in a carefully molded spherical sac. She drags the sac about with her and will defend it with her life. Like night-flying moths, the wolf spider is attracted to a black-light UV emitting bulb. The spider's spine sensors are on their legs and pedipalps. Spiders have no antennae. Some of the spines are probably dielectric antenna detectors for infrared emissions from chemical stimuli.

through the writings of these scientists: they all maintain that there may be an unknown electromagnetic force at work controlling the destinies of these small creatures. I will quote some of the more important observations concerning this fabulous sense.

C. V. Riley (1894), the famous American entomologist, in an uncanny prediction of things to come in the physical sciences, called this sense "telepathy," and stated:

> *But however difficult it may be to define this intuitive sense which, while apparently combining some of the other senses, may have attributes peculiar to itself, and however difficult it may be for us to analyze the remarkable sense of direction, there can be no doubt that many insects possess the*

Table 2

Scientists who have postulated electromagnetic detection or its equivalent by insects.

Author	Date	Terminology	Organ of detection	Profession of author
C.V. Riley	1894	Telepathy	Antennae	Entomologist
J.H. Fabre	1913	Hertzian waves	Antennae	Entomologist
? Noel	1915	Hertzian, X- or N-waves	Antennae	Entomologist
E.N. Marais	1937	Wireless	Antennae	Journalist & Attorney
L. Beck & W. Miles	1947	Infrared	Antennae	Professors
G.R.M. Grant	1948	Infrared	Antennae (pits)	Electrical Engineer
J. Duane & J. Taylor	1950	Infrared	Antennae	Chemists
B. Acworth	1955	Instinct	Antennae	Submarine Commmander
E.R. Laithwaite	1960	Infrared	Antennae	Electrical Engineer
P.S. Callahan	1964	Infrared	Antennae (spines)	Entomologist
R.H. Wright	1964	Infrared	Antennae	Physical Chemist

power of communicating at a distance, of which we can form some conception by what is known as telepathy in man. This power would seem to depend neither upon scent nor upon hearing in the ordinary understanding of these senses, but rather on certain subtle vibrations as difficult for us to apprehend as is the exact nature of electricity. [Emphasis mine.]

Notice that Riley says, "while apparently combining some of the other senses." He then goes on to say:

While having no sort of sympathy with the foolish notions that the spiritualists proclaim, to edify or terrify the gullible and unscientific, I am just as much out of sympathy with that class of materialistic scientists who refuse to recognize that there may be and are subtle physical phenomena beyond the reach of present experimental methods. The one class too readily assumes supernatural power to explain abnormal phenomena: the other denies the abnormal because it, likewise, is past our limited understanding. [Dr. Riley then quotes the inventor of the cathode ray tube, English chemist Sir William Crookes]: *"Even now,"* says *William Crookes, who speaks with authority, "telegraphing without wires is possible within a radius of a few hundred yards,"* and, *in a most interesting contribution to our present knowledge of vibratory motion and the possibilities of electricity, the same writer remarks, "The discovery of a receiver sensitive to one set of wavelengths and silent to others is even now partially accomplished. The human eye is an instance supplied by nature of one which responds to the narrow range of electromagnetic impulses between the three ten-millionths of a millimeter and the eight ten-millionths of a millimeter. It is not improbable that other sentient beings have organs of sense which do not respond to some or to any of the rays to which our eyes are sensitive,* but are able to appreciate other vibrations to which we are blind. *Such beings would practically be living in a different world from our own. Imagine, for instance, what idea we should form of surrounding objects were we endowed with eyes not sensitive to the ordinary rays of light, but sensitive to the vibrations con-*

cerned in electric and magnetic phenomena. Glass and crystal would be among the most opaque of bodies. Metals would be more or less transparent, and a telegraph wire through the air would be like a long, narrow hole drilled through an impervious solid body. A dynamo in active work would resemble a conflagration, while a permanent magnet would realize the dreams of medieval mystics and become an everlasting lamp with no expenditure of energy or consumption of fuel."[1] [Emphasis mine.]

Following Riley, the equally famous French entomologist, J. Henri Fabre (1913), who is often misquoted as believing only in scent, said in his masterful essay on the great peacock moth:

Physical science is today preparing to give us wireless telegraphy, by means of the Hertzian waves. Can the great Peacock have anticipated our efforts in this direction? In order to set the surrounding air in motion and to inform pretenders miles away, can the newly hatched bride have at her disposal electric or magnetic waves, which one sort of screen would arrest and another let through?

Fabre never decided to his own satisfaction whether it was scent alone or some special wavelength at work. He further says, concerning the lesser peacock moth:

Dinner is forgotten in the presence of the wonders that are taking place. With inconceivable punctuality, the plume-wearers hasten to answer the captive's magic call. They arrive one by one, with a tortuous flight. All of them come from the north. This detail has its significance. As a matter of fact, during the past week we have experienced a fierce return of winter. The north wind has been blowing a gale, killing the imprudent almond blossoms. It was one of those ferocious storms which, as a rule, usher in the spring in our part of the world. Today the temperature has suddenly grown milder, but the wind is still blowing from the north.
Now at this first visit, all the moths hurrying to the prisoner enter the enclosure from the north; they follow the movement of the air; not one beats against it. If their compass were a sense of smell similar to our own, if they were

guided by odoriferous particles dissolved in the air, they ought to arrive from the opposite direction. If they came from the south, we might believe them to be informed by effluvia carried by the wind; coming as they do from the north, the mistral — that mighty sweeper of the atmosphere — how can we suppose them to have perceived, at a great distance, what we can smell? This reflux of scented atoms in a direction contrary to the aerial current seems to me inadmissible.

In his classic work on tropisms and sense organs of Lepidoptera, N. E. McIndoo (1929) refers to Pruffer (1927) and Noel (1915) as follows:

Pruffer states that his results and those of Patijaud demonstrate that female moths cannot lure the males from long distances, in spite of evidence shown years ago by Forel, Fabre, and others. He says that the female of Saturnid pryi *L., as an example, can attract the males from a distance of not over 50 meters. Noel concluded that neither sight nor smell is sufficient to explain the attraction from long distances. As a hypothesis, he suggested that certain insects emit special waves or rays, resembling X-rays, or the Hertzian waves, or even the N-rays of Dr. Blondlot. He firmly believed that these rays, which have not yet been isolated or verified, really exist and that they are used in distant communication. It has also been suggested that the bushy antennae of certain moths support this theory.*

Marais (1937), in *The Soul of the White Ant*, writes the following about the termite:

When she has found a suitable spot, she does a very peculiar thing. She comes to rest on her forefeet and lifts three-quarters of the hinder part of her body into the air, and she remains stationary in this position, as still as if she were merely the statue of a termite. If you become impatient and walk away, the secret of the flying termite will remain a secret to you forever. What is she doing? She is busy sending a wireless SOS into the air.

Marais concluded that this SOS signal might be scent, but in Chapter III, he interprets scent in the same manner that I do, not as little bundles of matter to be collected in higher or lower concentrations by one antenna or the other as they contact the sensory organ, but, as he states:

> When speaking of scent you should again think of waves in the ether. It is false to assume that perfumes consist of gases or microscopic substances. Perfume itself is not entirely a physical substance. You may scent a large room for ten years with a small piece of musk and yet there will not be any loss in weight.

Keep this statement of Marais' in mind as I discuss my findings.

The term infrared radiation was not used until 1948, when G. R. M. Grant wrote a paper theorizing that the antennal pits of insects might be resonate cavities. He stated:

> The conditions for such transmission and resonance at the longest wavelength possible, are that the cross-sectional dimensions of the dielectric should be of the order of a wavelength. For any particular case, however, there are a number of other discrete wavelengths, shorter than the maximum, for which there occurs good transmission (or resonance), as the case may be. Each such wavelength bears a definite relation to the dimension of the cavity. The literature on pit-like sensilla of insects show that their transverse dimensions lie between 2 and 80 micrometers. Most of the energy radiated from bodies at normal temperatures is at wavelengths within this range.

G. R. M. Grant's work on dielectric pits was published in the Australian *Proceedings of the Royal Society of Queensland*. Grant is an electrical engineer, and wrote his paper in 1949 at almost the same time that I was doing my moth watching by candlelight in Italy. He had searched through the literature on insect antennae and had noted that many species have sensory pits in their antennae. He was intrigued by the minute dimensions of the pits, and theorized on the possibility of the sensory pits being dielectric pit resonators to infrared radiation.

He never experimented, or published another paper on the subject, and other than my theoretical and experimental work, his was the only correct approach to the idea that the insect might be able to detect radiations with its antennae. Like Laithwaite, however, Grant did not consider scent as the source of that radiation, for he wrote in his introduction:

> *The existence of a non-tactile sense of an obscure nature has been shown by many observers. It has been described as olfactory, but a dependence on a gaseous emanation had not been shown in many cases, nor had it been satisfactorily demonstrated upon which organs the supposed olfactory sense depends.*

The writings of all these gentlemen caused me to search the literature for behavioral patterns among insects that might indicate both an olfactory and an infrared basis for insect communication. I made up a table covering possible types of sensing and the authors who described them (see Table 3).

When I finished the review, I was more convinced than ever that the sensory mechanism was both infrared and olfactory — in short, that insects "smell" odors electronically by tuning into the narrowband infrared radiation emitted by sex and host-plant scents.

Neither Laithwaite nor Wright, both of whom believed that infrared radiation was involved in insect communication, paid the slightest attention to Grant's work. It was strange, for I believed that every one of these researchers was partially right and that only a synthesis of all their ideas would solve the problem. I had already measured the refractive index of the insect exoskeleton, and calculated the dielectric constant from that figure, and I knew that Grant's dielectric waveguide approach was the correct one.

After my first paper was published, I began a long correspondence with Dr. Ernest Okress, a brilliant electrical engineer. The correspondence gradually increased as he tutored me — through the mail — in waveguide theory. His knowledge of waveguide physics steered me on a level course through the difficulties encountered by a practical biologist working in a field that is considered theoretically complex, even by the best physicists. Dielectric waveguide theory is still of fairly recent interest to researchers and, as in the case of thermoelectrets, there are not a lot of scientists working in the field. Dr. Okress's help was invaluable, and I deeply appreciated it.

Table 3

A few areas where infrared radiations
probably play a significant role.

Insects	Area	Based on description of behavior by
Night-flying moths	Location of mates and host plants	P. S. Callahan, E. R. Laithwaite & others
Mosquitoes, Simuliidsa	Attraction to birds & mammals	A. W. A. Brown & others
Ticks	Attraction to mammals	W. A. Bruce & others
Wood-boring beetle	Attraction to forest fires	W. G. Evans
Horseflies, Deer flies	Attraction to animals, especially cows	A. J. Thorsteinson, G. K. Bracken & others
Wasps	Prey location, especially wood-boring and stalk-inhabiting prey	J. H. Comstock & P. S. Callahan
Ants	Behavior underground, mate location, foraging behavior	W. M. Wheeler, P. S. Callahan, J. C. Nickerson, & W. H. Whitcomb
Termites	Behavior underground and mate location	E. N. Marais
Predaceous spiders	Prey location at night	W. H. Whitcomb & others

It was a statement by C. H. Townes, the inventor of the laser, which further convinced me that I had the correct idea about emitting molecules. According to Townes, *Microwave Amplification by Stimulated Emission of Radiation* (maser), is a more common phenomenon of nature than researchers have ever suspected.

The maser (microwave) system was invented before the laser (light) system. Both, of course, work on the principle of oscillations from molecules being put in phase so that they emit their radiation in synchronization. Townes stated that we have probably had maser action all along in narrowband IR lines emitted by gas discharge tubes such as fluorescent lamps. His exact words are:

> For some systems a heavy discharge pulse in the gas is needed. Others, particularly some of the infrared frequencies in rare gases, oscillate so readily that it seems probable that we have had lasers accidentally all along. Very likely, some neon or other rare-gas electric signs have been producing maser oscillations at IR wavelengths, which have gone unnoticed because the IR cannot escape from the glass neon tube. [Emphasis mine.]

Townes made that statement in a paper in *Science* (1965) less than a year after I published my first theoretical paper relating the insect communication system to the infrared environment that surrounds this planet Earth.

I could not help but consider the many species of insects that are attracted to various gas discharge lamps and neon signs. I began to wonder how many maser lines do escape from the glass envelope. The obvious answer, of course, is that the moths are merely going to the fluorescent visible light — but how about all the infrared light we can't see coming from the tube? As I stated before, the obvious answer is not necessarily the correct answer.

A laser, or maser, is a resonating system, but to understand how mirrors act to get the infrared frequencies in phase, we must understand what fluorescence is. Sir William Crookes, quoted by the entomologist C. V. Riley, was the inventor of the cathode ray tube. Crookes studied science at the Royal College of Chemistry in London. His father willed him a fortune, so he was able to devote full time to his research. He worked with electrical discharges in rarefied gases, and developed a theory of "radiant matter" which he called matter in the fourth state. Even today, plasma is called the fourth state of matter. Plasma has many peculiar characteristics that are not physical properties of liquids, solids, or gases. Some of what Tesla accomplished with gas discharge tubes, including his high-energy X-ray studies, was based on Crookes's brilliant work. Crookes, incidentally, was not a materialistic scientist and he spent a considerable amount of time studying psychic phenomena. He sought to correlate the occult with the physical sciences, and maintained a belief in the occult until his death. As early as 1896, Crookes pointed out that the elements contain atoms of different atomic weights. He was also the first chemist to succeed in making artificial diamonds. Like Tesla, Sir William Crookes was a fascinating and complex individual.

As everyone knows, an atom is thought to consist of a central nucleus surrounded by electrons in different levels of orbit almost like our sun and its orbiting planets. These different layers of electrons are considered to be energy levels. In the normal state of equilibrium, all of the electrons stay put in their "natural" levels of orbit, as do our planets. My top drawing (see *Figure 12*) shows a hypothetical three-level energy state for a large group (called a population) of atoms. They are all in their normal equilibrium state. When energies from another source, such as an electrical discharge, impinge upon this population of atoms, the electrons orbiting each nucleus are raised from one energy level to a higher energy level. This phenomenon is called absorption by the atom or molecule. We might think of absorption as being the effect of an outside energy source that drives a significant population of little people from the first floor, called ground state, up to the third-floor level. As more and more of the little electron people reach the third floor, it finally gives way and they drop through the third floor to the second floor. In doing so, they give off heat and electrical energy, which is lost to the system. In some populations of atoms or molecules (combined atoms), the little electron people fall right through the second floor so fast that they reach the ground state without any further detectable energies being given off. However, in other atomic or molecular combinations, particularly in the gaseous state (remember, a scent is a complex gas), the second floor (energy level) is of such a character — like a strong oak floor — that many, many electron people pile up on the floor, and are held there for a much longer period of time before they break through the strong oak flooring and fall back to the ground level state. If the energy level second floor holds enough of the electron people for a long time, they pile up until the huge population that finally falls to the ground floor level gives off a tremendous burst of electromagnetic energy. While falling back to ground

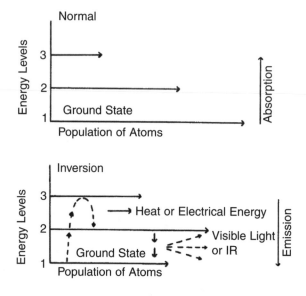

Figure 12. Energy level system for a hypothetical population of atoms. The top figure represents atoms with electrons in three levels at room temperature. In the standard model the electrons are pictured as orbiting around a nucleus at the different levels. As the atoms absorb radiation from an outside source, certain electrons move to high levels — go upstairs. Since the electrons tend to return to their normal level (reach equilibrium) they almost immediately drop back down giving off heat and electrical energy in the process (*bottom figure*). In certain cases they may linger at a second level and store up energy before dropping back to rest on the way to the ground floor — called the ground state. If enough of the electrons store up in this second level, called the metastable state, they may emit electromagnetic radiation as they finally drop to ground state. Such emitted radiation is called fluorescence and may be UV, visible or infrared in frequency. To laser atoms or molecules, fluorescence, which is incoherent radiation, must occur first.

level, this huge temporarily "stored" population emits either visible, UV, or infrared (light) frequencies. These frequencies are in different portions of the electromagnetic spectrum and depend on the makeup of the gas atoms or molecules involved.

Physicists call the second-floor storage level the *metastable* state. They have shown that to get lasting action, you must first have fluorescent frequencies given off as the electrons fall from the second floor metastable state to the ground state. If the emitted fluorescent light is red, green or other visible frequencies, we can detect these visible light energies with our eyes. There must be, however, as Dr. Townes pointed out, many fluorescent IR energies that we cannot detect with our eyes; we need complex infrared sensors to detect them. This is especially true of the far infrared, where radiations are very weak in terms of electron-volt energy. The mirrors in a laser are spaced so that they put all of these fluorescing electrons in phase, and they come out marching in synchronization, and thus are amplified.

It becomes obvious to me from reading physics that it takes a lot of energy going into a system to get visible fluorescence, which is fairly high-energy radiation, out. However, it does not take nearly as much energy going into a system to get low electron-volt IR fluorescent energy, out. Of course, we could not see such nebulous, glowing infrared fluorescing radiations because our eye is not tuned to them.

Physicists call the energy going into a system, *e.g.*, the electrical discharge of a helium-neon laser, the "pumping" energy. In the case of the ruby solid-state laser, which puts out a red coherent beam, the energy going in comes from a high-intensity visible flash lamp which causes the chrome impurities in the ruby to fluoresce. My studies of the mechanisms of visible and microwave lasers convinced me that very low quanta of energy from the sun, or even from the stars, moon or black body radiation of night light, might "pump" scent molecules so that they fluoresce in the far-infrared region of the spectrum. In other words, I believed that the gas did not need to be contained in a tube and pumped by a high electrical discharge, but that scent is, in essence, a free-floating fluorescence pumped by the natural day, night, sun and star, or the black body energies, of our spaceship Earth. Scent, in my mind, is a fleeting-floating world of vapors that luminesce in many, many different infrared colors and can be amplified and collected by a scent organ such as the insect antenna. The antenna sensilla are tuned as a resonating system to these IR frequencies. Accordingly, I coined the term "maser-like frequencies" for the scent infrared colors that we could not detect until the early 70s.

It may be observed from Table 2 that after the year 1915 not a single insect physiologist or biologist, other than myself (that I know of) considered that the insect communication system might involve electromagnetic radiation. From that year on, all the theorists were either unbiased amateur researchers, chemists, or electrical engineers. This should tell us something about becoming too specialized in a science.

In the next chapter we shall see how three significant experiments confirmed my theory on these maser-like infrared emissions and the dielectric antenna collectors of these nebulous radiations. It is a lesson in how a generalist can cut across fields to correlate many different and complex phenomena of nature. I succeeded because I am an amateur scientist — one who pursues science not for money or glory but because he loves it; that, after all, is the real definition of an *amateur*. All really good research scientists are amateurs because they love their work. It is only an accident of modern times that scientists are paid for working at their hobby. In previous ages, scientists like Sir William Crookes had to be independently wealthy to follow their research careers — or at least to have a rich patron as did Leonardo da Vinci.

The U. S. Department of Agriculture (USDA) paid me to watch moths at candles, and in following my research love (the taxpayers were my patrons), I eventually proved, as we shall see, how the candle as a generator of maser-like infrared frequencies attracts night-flying moths. It is to the tax payers' advantage to indulge my hobby, for it may lead to better methods of insect control and also to a better method of collecting energy for use in our homes.

Footnotes

[1]"Some Possibilities of Electricity" in *Fortnightly Review*, March, 1892. (Riley, p. 135).

The Love Bug Phenomenon

Chapter 9
The Love Bug Phenomenon

In 1966, Dr. Robert Berger, working at Auburn University in Alabama isolated the sex scent pheromones from the cabbage looper moth. Not only is the cabbage looper destructive to cabbage, broccoli and other cole crops; it also feeds on cotton plants. When Dr. Tom Henneberry, in California, placed the cabbage looper pheromones in a trap in a cotton field with an ultraviolet light (black light) above it, the catch of the night-flying cabbage loopers went up spectacularly. Often as many as six to ten times more moths were caught when the combination was used than were caught with the pheromones, or the black light, used separately in the field. Entomologists attributed the increase to the effect of two systems working on the moth through two separate senses — the light through the eye, and the pheromones through the antenna. My interpretation was entirely different, and the tremendous increase in catch only served to reinforce belief in my infrared theory of the insect dielectric antenna.

There are two very important threads that run through the observed behavioral responses of various insect species to different infrared radiating objects — especially the manmade objects. First, more infrared black body radiation is emitted from these objects than is radiation from the natural objects surrounding them, and second, these radiating black bodies are surrounded by innumerable scents from the fleeting-floating molecules of nature.

The infrared black body radiation from a moth's heated body is quite low; from a human body it is a little higher; from the heated surface of a tor on the Dartmoor yet higher; from a candle considerably higher; and highest of all from tungsten-filament light bulbs and fluorescent tubes such as blacklights and neon signs. If the black body radiation from the sun or night sky can be absorbed by scent molecules, as I believe it can, and the molecules stimulated to emit fluorescent infrared frequencies, then surely such luminescent scents in the presence of strong black body light bulbs, or fluorescent tubes, must be stimulated to an even higher state of excitation.

In my lab at Tifton, Georgia I set out to test my hypothesis that insect sex scents in the presence of strong black body radiation emit high-energy, maser-like radiation — higher than would ever occur in the natural state where the molecule is ordinarily stimulated by the night sky black body radiation.

I enclosed a six-watt black light bulb in an infrared filter that completely excluded all of the visible and black light UV from the bulb, and let through the infrared from 1 to 30 micrometers. The trap was placed in a 15' x 15' walk-in cold room set at a night temperature of 65°F. Each night, for five successive nights, I released 100 male fall armyworms into the totally dark, insulated room. At the end of the week only seven percent of the 500 moths had found their way into the radiating infrared trap. The next week, I put two virgin female moths in the trap, and replaced them with fresh females each night. I again released 100 male fall armyworm moths into the trap. In the next five nights I trapped 98 percent, or 490 of the 500 male moths released in the room. When I turned off the strong infrared black body light source in the trap so that the pheromone-releasing female moths were in total (no visible or IR) darkness, I did not trap a single male moth.

Insect physiologists have shown time and time again that the insect eye — particularly the moth's eye — has peaks of high sensitivity in the green and also in the black light UV (0.36 micrometer) portion of the spectrum. This is quite understandable because at night there is both a near-UV (black light) and a green-light air glow. The molecules in the night sky are stimulated to glow at these frequencies, and the sky glows perfectly match the vision of the moths. Of course we humans do not notice these glows because our eye cannot see UV as does the insect eye, and the green glow is too weak to see with our color vision which functions poorly at night.

I performed the same experiment with a small green bedroom nightlight, which also emitted tremendous amounts of black body infrared radiation. This time I used the corn earworm moth. In the presence of the green nightlight, and only one scent-emitting female, I trapped more than 80 percent of the male moths that I had released.

Dr. Wendell Snow, a colleague at the Tifton lab, agreed to set up some experiments to further test my theory of black body stimulation of pheromone emission. We built four boxes and lined two of them with aluminum foil. The other two we painted black. In one of the aluminum-lined boxes, and in one of the painted boxes, we placed a young corn plant. We lighted each of the boxes with a tungsten light bulb, the voltage cut down until it glowed very dimly with the approximate intensity of a starlit night, similar to a half moon in the sky. Although the aluminum-lined boxes resembled nothing less than mirrored fun houses, I reasoned that the highest mating should occur in them. As the female moths released their pheromones in the enclosed box, it would be radiated from all directions by the high-intensity black body IR reflecting from the mirrored walls and coming from the tungsten light bulb. The presence of the corn plant would assure a stable amount of water vapor in the boxes, and since plants are emitting black bodies, they should absorb and emit the IR radiation from the bulb, and also contribute to increased mating.

The lowest percentage of mating occurred in the black box without a corn plant. Only 31.8 percent of the female moths mated in that box. In the aluminum-lined box with the corn plant, 83.5 percent of the females mated. Actually it was a much higher percentage, for in this latter box 32.4 percent of the female corn earworms mated two or more times. In the aluminum-lined box without a corn plant, the percentage of mating was 73.7 percent, and 20.4 percent had mated more than once. The experiment had worked exactly as predicted for there was a much higher incidence of mating in both of the aluminum boxes. The experiment also demonstrated one of the paradoxes of entomological research. From times long past, insect behaviorists, and I am one, have painted their moth cages black inside because that color supposedly resembles nighttime. It decidedly does not, because the black paint instead absorbs most of the infrared radiation, while the night sky definitely does not — the night sky emits IR.

I am sure that by this time the reader is wondering how on Earth an entomologist can know how many times a moth has mated without staying up night after night to watch the sexual occurrence. When I was doing research for my Ph.D. degree, I did indeed stay up night after night watching and describing the nighttime sexual activities of the corn earworm moth — in fact, in the 1950s I became known to my fellow graduate students at Kansas State University as the sex expert of the moth world.

It did not take me long to discover, by reading early 19th Century literature, that amateur collectors studying the life history of butterflies and moths found that the male moth transfers the sperm to the female in a peculiar packaged container — a protein capsule called a spermatophore. In noctuids, the protein capsule resembles a ball with a long neck and a hook at the aperture end of the neck. It required half my Ph.D. dissertation to describe the sexual behavior of the night-flying noctuid moth.

Strangely enough, although noctuids are the most destructive of our agricultural insects, nobody had ever bothered to describe in detail how they mate. Working on my Ph.D., I set out to do just that. I learned that it took the male moth up to an hour to transfer the sperm-filled spermataphore to the female.

Male moths have a pair of hook-like claspers, which are normally retracted into the abdomen. Once attracted to the female by her pheromones, the male clasps the tip of her abdomen with his claspers and slowly ejects the formed spermatophore from his reproductive duct into an expanded organ of her reproductive system called a *bursa copulatrix*. (See *Figures 13 & 14*.)

After a female had died, days later, I discovered how to dissect her and count the number of empty spermatophores in order to determine how many times she had mated. Today this is a common method of studying reproduction in insects that pass spermatophores.

Years ago, when I worked on moth reproduction, my life became somewhat more nocturnal than usual. In the evening after classes, my wife left for her job at the hospital, and I, in charge of two baby daughters — one under each arm — walked to the insectary. There the two cherubs crawled and toddled about on the concrete floor, investigating each nook and cranny of the screened building, as often as not sampling old pieces of yellowed corn ears, or picking up an earworm that had fallen on the floor to pop into their mouths. Today I attribute their robust health to the protein and trace elements thus obtained.

How many researchers and scholars have contributed to the total knowledge of the world under these same conditions will probably never be known. Certainly, following World War II, more than a million young Americans who had marched off to fight the most ferocious war in the history of mankind, returned to involve themselves in the largest effort of mass education ever attempted. It is the fallacious belief of each generation that it is far more sophisticated and wiser than the preceding generation, and for the older generation to believe that the younger is, without a doubt, a huge conglomeration of wild-eyed delinquents. One who studies history knows that the generation gap is no greater today than it was in the time of Caesar — just better advertised by the media. Whatever is wrong with America today, however, cannot be laid at the feet of those returning GIs, for they marched into the "Halls of Ivy" less inhibited, more tolerant, more willing to learn, and with greater imagination and desire for new experimentation than any group of human beings on the face of the Earth. These scholars and thinkers of many diverse fields of endeavor were to be found on every university campus, and in every business or government agency. They were the scientists, engineers, business leaders and government people who have helped to bring about what today is called the "information era."

Figure 13. Claspers of the male corn earworm month. The center organ, called an *aedeagus*, is the outer phallus. The male clasps the tip of the female abdomen with the claspers during copulation.

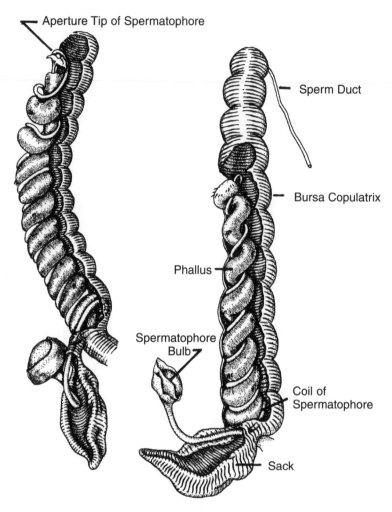

Figure 14. Cut away view of the female *bursa copulatrix* showing the male *phallus* expanded into the bursa and ejecting the coiled proteinaceous sperm container called a *spermatophore*. The phallus feeds the forming spematophore out of its tip and in a coil back down along itself until the *bulb* end, containing the sperm, reaches the *sack*-like side arm of the bursa (*bottom*) where it expands into a round bulb. The process takes about an hour. The male pulls its phallus free by everting it (like turning a glove inside out) leaving the spermatophore inside the female bursa. On the right the phallus is shown expanding into the bursa. On the left it is all the way in, leaving the *aperture tip* of the long coiled spermatophore at the tip of the bursa (*top*). When the phallus is withdrawn, the spermatophore tip remains against the *sperm duct* that leads from the top of the bursa to the oviduct where the eggs are stored.

144   *Tuning in to Nature*

Whatever is right with the country is right because of them, and much of what is right with the generations to come will be so because they passed on a bit of their thinking to their offspring. In a very few decades, more has been learned of life and man than in all the preceding years of man's long evolutionary history.

No less a credit to their country were those "wives of the tar paper shacks" that covered every campus of every state university in America. These were the frontier women of the forties and fifties. They could not shoot a gun or defend their homes from marauders or plow a field, but they could work and forego all comforts; they could type their husband's thesis, care for his children, put food on the table, and at the same time earn the money for both the table and the food. They were a laughing, happy lot of females who seldom complained, for they fought to keep their husbands on the educational battlefield. Some of them went to school when they could, but, school or not, they educated themselves, for they were as much a part of campus life as the chemistry lab and assistant professors. No committee of sociologists, no government agency or group of researchers will ever be able to measure the contribution of those "wives of the tar paper shacks"; they will never get medals for their bravery, or have songs written about them; all we can do is love them and treat them gently for what they gave to their country.

Not too long after I ran my moth experiments, I went to an electronics meeting in Chicago where the prototype of an instrument called a Fourier transform interferometer was on display. I had read about the new Fourier transform technique of obtaining infrared emission spectra from weak infrared sources, so I carried my green nightlight, some peanuts and a candle to the meetings. A friend of mine, Bud Redlinger, and I had been running experiments with a moth, called the Indian meal moth, that attacks stored peanuts. During the experiments, we discovered that they mated exceptionally well in the presence of, and were attracted to, the green light, a candle or to slightly warmed peanuts. (See *Figure 15*.)

The scientist from Block engineering, the company that made the interferometer part of the system, ran my warm peanuts, candle and green light. All three emitted considerable black body infrared radiation in the 6- to 20-micrometer part of the spectrum. Unfortunately at that time the instrument was not high-resolution

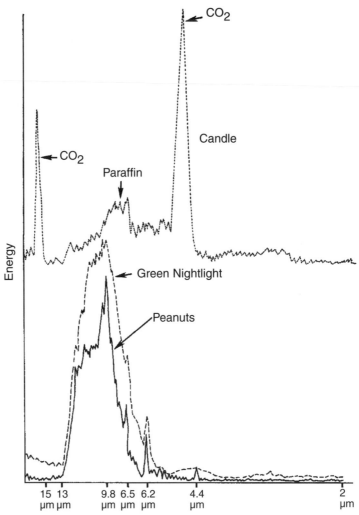

Figure 15. Comparison of the infrared emission from a candle (*top*), green night light (*middle*) and warm peanuts (*bottom*). The candle gives off tremendous energy from heated CO_2 molecules at 4.4 and 15μm. Small CO_2 peaks also seen at 4.4μm coming from the green night light and peanuts. The latter two emitters give off considerable black body radiation between 6 and 13μm in the 7 to 14μm atmospheric window, as does the paraffin (hydrocarbons) from the candle. The jagged peak of all three emitters indicate many narrow band sharp frequency lines concealed in the broad black body spectrum shown here. Such sharp lines are like the color lines that make up visible white light but which must be filtered out for us to see as narrow band colors. The green nightlight also, of course, gives off a green glow far to the right at 0.5μm. The Indian meal moth is attracted to all three of these emitters which have peaks in the 10μm far IR region.

enough to see if the broadband black body energy also contained narrowband IR lines. Like a nearsighted person, it only saw the spectrum as a sort of hazy broadband curve, and not as a series of sharply defined IR bands or lines. At any rate, I was encouraged, and decided on the spot to obtain the instrument as soon as it was perfected. It was quite obvious that each of the three IR transmitters emitted strong black body curves, and that the jagged curve indicated that each had significant narrowband emission lines in the same parts of their spectra.

Shortly after I moved to the new USDA Insect Attractant and Behavior Laboratory in Gainesville, Florida, the State of Florida became concerned with a strange wetland fly. It is called the "love bug," because the male and female are always seen together in the act of copulation.

I have been familiar with this interesting creature since boyhood when I spent summers on the gulf coast of Mississippi with my family. Later, when I was teaching at Louisiana State University, I often drove to Plaquemines Parish, south of New Orleans, to test insecticides in plots at the vegetable experiment station.

The love bug emerges twice a year from its habitat, which is mainly old rotting grass and organic matter in low damp areas. In May and September, during the peak of love bug flight, the windshield of my car would be covered with the smashed bodies of the little black flies. For some strange reason, there always seemed to be more of them flying in mating pairs over the highway than in the fields or woods beside the highway. The larvae of this insect are very beneficial and aid in recycling rotting organic matter. The paired adults were a nuisance, but I considered them useful as they caused me to stop quite regularly for a windshield washing and a cup of coffee. After a tiring day in the field, starting at five o'clock in the morning, stopping often was a safety factor in avoiding fatigue. In a car that is metal, one is cut off from the natural 200-volt field that a six-foot man walks around in on the surface of the Earth. There is some evidence from space work to show that this is not good for long periods of time, and may lead to fatigue sooner than is normal.

At any rate, the folk of southern Louisiana paid little heed to the swarms of love bugs over their highways, and looked upon them, as I did, as an excuse to stop for a cup of coffee — in that part of our country — and I might add, the best coffee in the world.

If the people of southern Louisiana were not concerned with the great flights of love bugs over their highways in May and September, the same cannot be said of the masses of migratory northern tourists who travel each year down the interstate highways to Disney World in central Florida. In one particularly bad season, the Governor of Florida received more than 400 letters from irate travelers who thought that Florida should clean up its buggy state. The love bug phenomenon is a wonderful example of urban thinking regarding insects in general.

My friend, Harold Denmark, was Director of Entomological Research for the State of Florida. Naturally enough, the job fell to him to find out what could be done to keep the tourists happy. The tourist trade is a good part of Florida's income, and like every other entomologist in the state, Harold Denmark was not too enthusiastic about spraying thousands of miles of highway right-of-ways, even if it would work, which was not likely.

I had never believed that insect control should depend on insecticides, and in fact I left Louisiana State University for that very reason. Long before I left, and also long before Rachel Carson published her book, *Silent Spring* in 1962, I took DDT out of the control recommendations for all of the vegetable crops under my research domain in Louisiana. I substituted biodegradable insecticides that break down in the environment. I was by no means the only state or federal entomologist of that persuasion — the USDA spends far more money researching alternate ways to control insects than it spends on insecticide research. As a matter of fact, for the record, when Dr. H. C. Cox, director of the Tifton, Georgia lab, hired me with the approval of Drs. Reynold Dahms and Phil Luginbill — the two branch leaders for forage crop research — I was promised that I would be left alone to study my moths and candles full time. I was hired as an insect ecologist, and throughout my career as a federal scientist not a single USDA administrative director (including those at both labs where I worked) had ever interfered with my research — this, in spite of the fact that the "physiological" insect olfaction experts around the world think I am wasting my time, and my name does not appear in most publications of the group.

The USDA has several entomology research labs, scattered around the country, and the quality of research performed by its scientists is on a par with the best anywhere in the world. I could write three more chapters listing the accomplishments of USDA entomologists. Like the scientists in NASA, they do their jobs well, as do most civil servants, with little fanfare or credit for their work.

Harold Denmark, the Florida entomologist whom I was just referring to before I got off the track, is also a naturalist. Although he is the administrator of his department, he is a very careful observer of nature. He walked into my office one day and asked if I would help him research an observation he had made on love bugs. I was somewhat startled when he said he firmly believed that the love bug is attracted to automobile exhaust fumes over the highway. He had noticed that whenever he started his lawnmower, the love bugs in his yard headed for the area of the exhaust pipe. I hadn't thought about the love bug except to observe that it did the traveler a favor by making him stop to clean his windshield, or to get a cup of coffee — no telling how many lives the love bug may have saved by making tourists reduce speed on the interstate system. (The higher the speed, the more the love bugs splatter.)

It didn't take more than 30 seconds of thinking for me to convince myself that Harold Denmark was right.

Insects, when they fly, vibrate their antennae at the same frequency that they flap their wings. They also spend a lot of time rubbing their antennae. I was certain that the antenna vibrations modulate the incoming infrared signals from scent molecules. The rubbing, I believed, cleans debris from the antenna surface and sweeps water moisture from the waxy antenna. Even more important, I was positive that all the rubbing insects do (watch a fly rubbing its front and hind legs together), somehow or other enters into the sensory mechanism. Much later, this hypothesis was independently supported by Ulrich Warnke, a German scientist, who wrote about this in a chapter from *Electromagnetic Bio-Information* (1989).

When Harold Denmark told me about his lawnmower, I could visualize the hot, vibrating metal, black body gas motor modulating some infrared frequency from the exhaust fumes, which is the same as a natural molecular frequency utilized by love bugs in their communication system. Since love bugs fly about in conjugal bliss, it could not be a frequency from a sex-scent involving pheromones. We reasoned that it must be an oviposition attractant — a frequency that tells the female where to lay her fertilized eggs.

We installed a long wooden flight box in my lab and collected some rather dirty exhaust from an old pick-up truck. I was not really disappointed when the love bugs sat placidly in the box and failed to fly to the end, where the exhaust was being emitted from our plastic bag. The box was covered with a glass top and lighted by overhead lab lights.

I suggested that we try both a tungsten light bulb (high IR source) and a black light UV bulb in combination with the exhaust fumes. First, as a check, we tried each light source separately and obtained no attraction whatsoever. The tungsten light bulb was no better when we blew the exhaust across it. When we blew the exhaust across the UV black light bulb, however, we got instantaneous almost violent results. We had put 20 pair in the box, and within seconds all twenty flew straight to the UV exhaust-fume source. Neither the UV bulb, nor the exhaust by itself, attracted a single pair. We repeated the experiment over and over with identical results.

The attraction to auto exhaust irradiated by black light UV was so predictable that when Walter Cronkite's TV crew read about our experiments in the *Tampa Tribune*, they asked if they could film an experiment for the evening news. We had no qualms at all about assuring them that the insects would perform like trained dogs. The TV crew drove down from Atlanta and, sure enough, 100 pair of the love bugs flew straight to the irradiated exhaust fumes.

The implications of this experiment were apparent from the literature of smog pollution research. The daylight UV that penetrates the ozone layer in the near UV at 0.36 micrometers is in the same frequency range as that emitted by our black light bulb. It is well known that auto exhaust, irradiated by sky UV, undergoes photochemical transformation to form smog. Some of the main chemical products of the reaction are aldehydes. Aldehydes are also emitted by piles of rotting organic matter where the love bugs lay their eggs. When we irradiated formaldehyde with the black light, the insects flew directly to the combination just as they did to the exhaust fumes.

Again, neither the UV bulb nor formaldehyde alone would attract the insect. This, then, was the daylight counterpart of the pheromones irradiated by the night-sky black body, and emitting fluorescent frequencies. I was certain that the daylight UV was stimulating the aldehyde by-product of smog formation, to fluoresce infrared frequencies somewhere in the water vapor windows, and that the exhaust was thus mimicking the maser-like infrared signal from aldehydes produced in the piles of rotting grass and cow manure where the female love bug preferred to lay her eggs.

The only difference between the moth and the love bug was the stimulating frequencies. In the case of the nocturnal moth, I believed it was the night-sky infrared black body radiation that "pumps" the emitted narrowband infrared pheromone frequency, whereas in the case of the love bug — a diurnal or day-flying insect — the day sky UV "pumps" certain narrowband infrared fluorescent frequencies coming from the aldehydes.

Harold Denmark, the naturalist, had brought me one more case of the attraction force inherent in mixing a known source of radiation with a known type of attractant molecule. In each case the attraction was extremely high, and in each case I knew I was one step closer to tuning in to nature.

Tuning in to the Pheromone

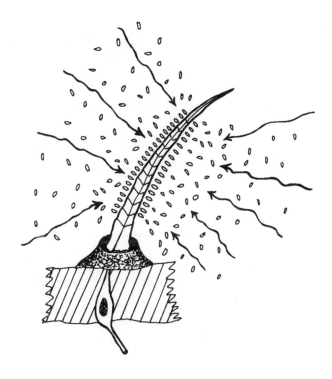

Chapter 10

Tuning in to the Pheromone

To prove my thesis that fleeting-floating scent molecules emit infrared maser-like frequencies like so many windblown satellites, I acquired some very specialized infrared detection equipment. Although the science of insect morphology, as applied to the insect dielectric antenna, told me where to look for frequencies, it certainly did not prove that the frequencies exist. To prove the whole thesis, I would have to detect the frequency output in a predictable region. Not only must the frequencies be detected, but the detection must be repeatable, or as scientists say, replicable. Science, if practiced honestly, is a self-correcting profession. Acceptable experimentation means repeatability of an experiment under prescribed conditions. The formula for the practice of science is:

$$\text{Hypothesis} \longrightarrow \text{Theory} \longrightarrow \text{Prediction} \longrightarrow$$
$$\text{Experimentation} \longrightarrow \text{Replication}$$

The chain is not complete without the last requirement, for if an experiment cannot be duplicated, then in all probability, the described phenomenon is either an artifact, or an exception to the norm. Obviously the signal of a communication system must be repeatable, or it is not a communication system. It is this last requirement that makes research into a phenomenon such as ESP so difficult, and also controversial. ESP is a form of communication, and yet experimentation is practically impossible to replicate. The phenomenon has to be treated with some rather complex statistics, for it appears to occur in certain individuals rather convincingly, but only on rare occasions. Although such a statistical treatment may indicate that ESP is a real phenomenon of nature, it never really proves its existence. In my opinion, researchers interested in ESP should attempt to find out how it works instead of trying to prove that it exists.

A prerequisite for repeatability, or replication, of an experiment is that the conditions of the experiment should be rigidly controlled, and the instrumentation accurately defined. The requirements imposed on my own experiments were that I not only obtain the correct instrument for detection, but that I should also treat the scent molecule in exactly the same way the insect does. This means not only a knowledge of the morphology of the moth antenna, but also of moth behavior.

In 1966, I finished the complete morphology of the corn earworm and cabbage looper antennae. Thelma Carlysle and I spent a lot of time taking measurements of the arrangement of the little sensilla spines on the main support axis of the antennae. The noctuid moth antenna comprises 80 to 90 segments strung together like beads. Each segment (bead) has many, many different types of sensors. One type, called a coeloconica by insect morphologists, I named the "picket fence" sensor because it is a corrugated peg with nerves, surrounded by a circle of spines arranged like the pickets of a fence. Since this is a circular, vectored configuration, I consider that perhaps it is the sensor that tunes into the vectored ILS (instrument landing system) black body radiation from the flapping moth described in Chapter 5. The vectored radiation from a wing-modulated female impinging on the central peg is possibly decoded by the angle of arrangement of the circle of pegs that surrounds it. There is no way to be sure of this, of course, unless maybe a way is figured out how to radiate the peg with a vectored source and get nerve impulses — a very difficult procedure since the sensory peg is surrounded by the pickets.

The main types of spine sensilla on the noctuid moth antenna are called trichodea from the Greek word trichodes, meaning hairlike. There are three general lengths of trichodea sensilla on moths: long (30- to 55-µm in length), medium (15- to 30-µm) and short (7- to 15-µm). The long trichodea of the cabbage looper moth are known, from the observance of nerve impulses, to respond to the cabbage looper pheromone isolated by Berger in 1966. There are

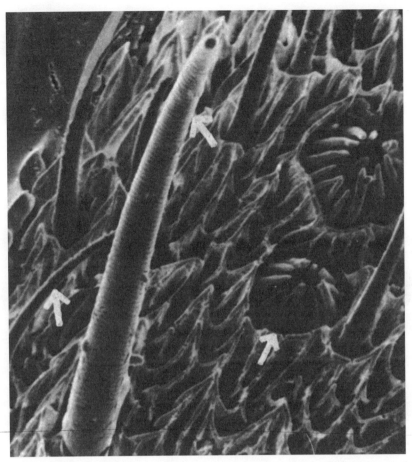

Sensory sensilla on the antenna of the male cabbage looper moth. The top arrow points to the longest type sensilla called a *chaetica*. It has a *terraced* sculpturing on the surface and an aperture at the tip. The IR electromagnetic waves focus at the aperture where the detector and nerve endings are located. The arrow on the left points to a spine-like curved trichodea (the basal portion of other trichodea can also be seen). The long curved trichodea sense the 17μm maser-like log-periodic IR from the sex pheromone of the female cabbage looper moth. The arrow on the right points to the picket fence sensilla called a *coeloconica*. The center peg which is corrugated is innervated by nerve endings. The surrounding pickets are solid and have no nerves. This may be the detector that senses the modulated broadband black body IR radiation from the flapping moth. It is a vectored (compass point) configuration and the black body radiation from the moth emits both a compass point (azimuth) and glide path (altitude) vector which makes the signal an excellent ILS (Chapter 5). This same vectored black body modulated IR signal is inherent in the flickering candle flame, as is each of the 17μm maser-like narrowband log periodic frequencies (Table 5) from the female sex pheromone.

more than three thousand of these sensilla on the cabbage looper moth antenna, and at least 2,500 on the antenna of the corn earworm moth. The main difference between the trichodea of each species is in curvature and diameter. In both species, the sensilla are arranged in definite patterns. We call such a pattern arrangement in antenna design, an array. As in the case of an indoor TV antenna which can be adjusted to increase reception, different insects have their trichodea sensilla arranged in different arrays.

When I measured the distance of the trichodea sensilla, I found that their lengths gradually increased or decreased depending on which end of the insect you start from. This arrangement of sensillae in gradually changing lengths satisfies one of the characteristics of a log-periodic antenna. A second characteristic of a log-periodic antenna is that as the antenna elements decrease in length, the distance between these individual elements also decreases. In other words, for our insect example, the spacing is not the same between the sensilla of each segment, but the sensilla are placed closer and closer together along each segment from the base to the tip. A logarithmic scale is a scale in which the actual distances from the base of the antenna is proportional to the logarithm of the spacing between the sensilla from segment to segment. It is not necessary to understand logarithms to visualize such an antenna. The photograph of the small microwave antenna, manufactured by Sylvania, shows the metal elements of a log-periodic antenna being assembled. Note that the elements are closer and closer together, and shorter and shorter from base to tip. Note also, as in the case of the insect dielectric antenna, that all of the elements are tapered.

A log-periodic antenna is sometimes referred to as a broadband antenna. Each antenna element is scaled so that it fits a group of frequencies as one tunes across a band from wavelength to wavelength. The design or, as we biologists say, the *morphology* (form) of the array told me that I should expect the cabbage looper, or corn earworm, fleeting-floating pheromone to emit infrared radiation in a series of log-periodic frequencies. In other words, during an equal time spread — say at five minute intervals — each wavelength should shift log-periodically to longer and longer wavelengths. The longer elements are scaled to "grab" or collect the longer wavelengths, and the shorter and shorter sensilla to grab the shorter and shorter wavelengths.

I knew that since the dielectric spine sensilla are open resonators, the longer ones, which respond to the phero- mone gas, should be more than one wavelength long — most likely, since they are tapered to cut down side-lobe interference, they should be at least two wavelengths long. Since they averaged from 30- to 55-micrometers long, I decided that I should look for infrared emissions from the fleeting-floating scent pheromone between 15 and 30-µm long.

When I finished my measurements in 1965-66, I wrote a paper in which I pointed out the log-periodic characteristic of the moth antenna. I also learned for the first time about a partial 15- to 26-micrometer IR water vapor window. It is a partial window, because it does have some very weak water vapor absorption lines in it. These weak absorption lines are twenty-two in number, and stretch between 17 and 18 micrometers. They were plotted and described by the National Bureau of Standards in 1962.

When I was invited by the Institute of Electrical and Electronic Engineers to present a paper at their annual conference on Engineering in Medicine and Biology in 1966 in San Francisco, I included the log-periodic characteristic of the noctuid moth antenna in that paper.

From years of observing and photographing insects in flight, or ants "trail following," I know, as mentioned in Chapter 9, that all insects vibrate their antennae while searching the environment. The vibration frequencies lie in the audio range between a few cycles-per-second (cps) up to 500 cps and more (for some midges). Ants and butterflies vibrate in the range from 5 to 20 cps; moths 30 to 60, and the faster wing-flapping wasps, bees and flies, 150 to 500 cps (see Table 4.)

Astronomers modulate weak infrared frequencies from space by vibrating the mirror of their interferometer detectors at audio frequencies. The audio-frequency vibration content of the infrared between 1 to 30 micrometers (where the sensilla trichodea should resonate), lies between 1 to 250 cps — the same range at which insects vibrate their antennae.

In 1970, I obtained one of the first three Fourier transform interferometers built by the Digilab Corporation of Cambridge, Massachusetts. The delivery of the complex instrument was a disaster. The company shipped it by van, and the drivers had allowed it to roll around on casters on the truck bed. With our help, Digilab

Table 4

Approximate Antenna Vibration Frequency
of Various Insect Groups

Insect Group	Frequency Range in cps (cycles per second)
Saturniid moths	8 - 16
Butterflies	8 - 21
Ants	12 - 20
Dragonflies	20 - 28
Sphingid moths	26 - 45
Noctuid moths	35 - 55
Crane flies	44 - 73
Lady beetles	80 - 85
Horse flies	96 - 100
Yellow jackets	110 - 115
Love bugs	126 - 140
Bumble bees	130 - 140
Fruit flies	150 - 250
Honey bees	185 - 190
Mosquitoes	200 - 500

spent the next year rebuilding the instrument. They replaced the parts piece by piece until I had an entirely different instrument without a single component of the original one.

The first produced type of any complex system is a prototype and, accordingly, a researcher has the usual amount of frustrations working with such an instrument. Nevertheless, the instrument eventually proved its worth, and was the only system capable of looking at narrowband infrared emissions from molecules with a fast enough scan-time to insure success.

The Fourier transform system that I had was a marriage of a triglycinesulphate detector with electronics, optics, a laser, an interferometer, and finally, a computer. It was a complex system, and as a biologist I often felt much as the launch crew at NASA might have felt in the early days of rocketry. So many systems are involved that some part is always down. With Dr. Ken Turner and Felix Lee, our electronic technician, I spend three-fourths of my research time fixing or tuning up the system. Sometimes it would be months before I could run a spectrum. Of course, like the

Corn earworm moth feeding on honeydew from a head of Bahia grass. The moth sucks the dew up through its uncoiled proboscis. This was an exceedingly difficult photograph to come by, because corn earworm moths seldom feed in daylight. Notice that the moth is not flying, nor are its wings vibrating, yet there is definite vibration of the antennae. Since the photograph was taken at $1/60$ of a second, the vibration frequency is above 60 beats per second. Among noctuid moths, the vibration frequency for modulating maser-like IR frequencies from food is apparently higher than the frequencies for modulating sex pheromones, which is below 60 in the cabbage looper and corn earworm moths. The tattered wings indicate that this is an old moth. The antennae of flying moths in other photographs in this book are not blurred, for they were taken with a photographic strobe light at $1/2000$ of a second, which froze the vibrations.

Saturn rocket, the system has been gradually perfected, modified and improved until, in today's technological era, one of my former students, Dr. Thomas Dykstra, has a system in his laboratory which is not much bigger than a printer and scans a given sample in about one second.

My research had led me down a long involved trail through the sciences of biology, physics and electrical engineering, and I was about to become involved in the science of physical chemistry. All of my previous work told me exactly where and how to look for the predicted log-periodic emissions. The dielectric constant measurements told me that the material from which the sensilla are formed should cause them to resonate in the infrared region of the spectrum. The length and diameter of the sensilla indicated the 15- to 30-micrometer range, as did the vibrating frequency of the moth antenna. Since the cabbage looper pheromone had been isolated and synthesized by chemists, and since I had already measured the cabbage looper antenna vibrations, at 50 to 55 cps, I planned to utilize the cabbage looper pheromone in my definitive experiments.

The sculpturing of the sensilla trichodea told me that the surface was typical of a type of open resonator waveguide in which little or no electromagnetic loss would be expected. The number and arrangement of the long sensilla trichodea told me that the antenna is an array, and since the spacing is approximately log-periodic, from base to tip, that the antenna is a broadband array, probably resonating to a series of timed log-periodic emissions. All of these structural assumptions were described and published before 1967, and were based on the material make-up, form and arrangement of the sensilla alone — in short, on the science of morphology.

My next two criteria for testing the cabbage looper pheromone were based on the behavior of the insect. Since insects of different species and families vibrate their antennae at different frequencies, and since all insects (except in low insect orders such as the *collembola*) have a vibration sensor called a Johnston's organ at the base of the antenna, I planned to look for fluorescence in the gas phase. If I found it, I would then vibrate a reed in the radiation field to see if I could get increased output and better detection by modulating the fluorescing signal.

Now nerve impulses are generated when the antenna is bent or vibrated. Back in the 1960s I was convinced that the Johnston's

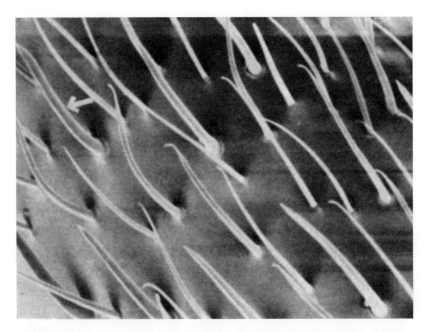

Short, tapered trichodea sensilla on the antenna of the fire ant. Four different types are shown here: 1) Short, straight with rounded tip; 2) long, slightly curved with sharp tip; 3) long, slightly curved and very thin; 4) (arrow) sickle-shaped. Moths follow scent trails through the air, ants follow scent trails laid along the ground. Although these ants do not fly, they still vibrate their antenna at from 12 to 20 cps while "trail following," so are without a doubt modulating maser-like frequencies from the trail scent.

organ was utilized by the insect to sense the correct antenna-vibration frequency, and to send a feedback signal to the brain so that the wing vibration muscles can set the correct modulation-vibration range while the insect flies through the IR-luminescing scent. Entomologists have since discovered that the Johnston's organ senses pressure waves, and in the case of the mosquito, these pressure waves emanate from the wingbeat frequency of the female. As I had earlier surmised, Johnston's organ was intimately tied to wingbeat frequencies, but whereas I felt they had more to do with molecular infrared emissions from sex pheromones, the conclusion drawn from the work on the mosquito claimed only that the male used Johnston's organ for direct sexual recognition. No mention, and assumedly no understanding of how wingbeat frequencies as it relates to infrared emissions from the fleeting-floating world, was discussed in the papers, nor is it mentioned in the classroom in today's universities. I felt it would be important for me to look at the sex pheromone with my new laboratory toy to see what would happen when I modulated the molecule with the wingbeat frequency of the cabbage looper which, as I have just mentioned, should be between 50 and 55 cps. But how should I go about this?

The last behavioral pattern of insects to intrigue me is the constant rubbing and cleaning of the antenna by all species of arthropods — spiders included. Since the antenna, as pointed out in Chapter 7, is an electret, and electrets attract molecules to their surface, it seemed logical to me that an insect flying through a long air stream of wind-carrying molecules would collect them as thin layers (monolayers, chemists call them) on the sensilla surfaces. Ulrich Warnke demonstrated how electrostatic effects influence deposition of a molecule on a pointed structure the size of an insect sensilla, and as in the case of the gas, the molecules would be thinly spread, and thus I felt there would be enough degrees of freedom between each molecule for it to vibrate and rotate and emit the characteristic frequencies. Chemists working on thin organic monolayers that fluoresce in the visible region, have shown that such thin layers emit narrowband (coherent) radiation just like an antenna.

Dr. Ursula Jander, in an excellent study of grooming and rubbing behavior throughout the orders of insects, has shown that the more active an insect species is, the more it grooms the antenna. Thelma Carlysle and I had already demonstrated experimentally that noctuids clean debris from their antennae in flight with an organ called the epiphysis on their forelegs. However, I felt that more than cleaning was involved in the rubbing, which occurs while insects are searching their environment for sex, or host-plant, scents.

The possibility that rubbing the antenna, as an insect does, will result in suppressing or amplifying pheromone signals, is dependent on the thermoelectret charge of the antenna, and the fact that a particle passing near and attached to the charge, so that it lands on the sensilla, will affect the thermoelectret properties of the antenna. Since I consider that the molecule must be extremely close to, or conversely, a thin layer bonded onto the sensilla surface, the rubbing of the antenna is quite likely to either dissipate the molecules or, conversely, with the proper amount of rubbing, line the molecules up in phase like soldiers marching in ranks —

in other words, to put them in coherence, or partial coherence, so that the electromagnetic infrared waves march down the sensilla in unison. The superimposed charge placed on the thermoelectret is analogous to the mirrors at either end of a gas laser: it puts the fluorescing layer into resonance so that the radiation leaving the molecule is narrowband and highly amplified as it travels down the wax-coated, resonating sensilla surface to the pore detectors. The 50 cps modulation frequency amplifies the signal therefore making it more easily detectable.

My experiments followed that reasoning and, as predicted, I found fluorescence exactly where I had expected it — in the gas phase. When I modulated the gas by vibrating a reed in the gas, the emission was 10 to 20 times stronger and easier to detect. When I rubbed a monolayer of the pheromone on the surface of a dielectric substance (such as beeswax or even a reflecting mirror), and modulated the thin layer by vibrating the mirror at 50 to 55 cps, I obtained high-energy narrowband maser-like coherent radiation (see *Figures 16-19*). Contrary to what I was led to believe after talking with chemists, each and every one of my predictions was correct. In experiments repeated over and over again, with both real and synthetic pheromones (the pheromone sample was first checked to make sure it attracted moths in the field), I observed log-periodic infrared emissions at 17- to 18- and 26- to 27-micrometer wavelengths. These frequencies match the two wavelength design criteria of the long 30- to 55-micrometer sensilla trichodea.

These emissions are quite easily amplified by rubbing, and by modulating a gas or a thin layer of molecules at 50 to 55 cps. Furthermore, the emission can be squelched by excessive rubbing of the thin layer. The probability of these emissions occurring where I had predicted, and "fitting" the morphology and behavior of the insect so perfectly, yet being coincidental, stretches the long arm of coincidence almost beyond belief.

After twenty-one years of experimentation, I had succeeded in "*tuning in to nature*." My theories had been proven valid by finding the exact log-periodic radiation where and how I had predicted and described it nine years previously.

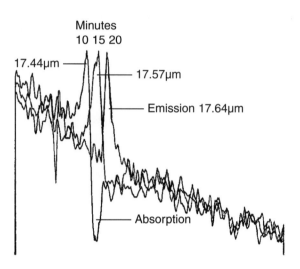

Figure 16. Log-periodic fluorescent emission from the cabbage looper pheromone (female sex scent). These are the real spectra from the scent enclosed in a glass cell. They were taken 5 minutes apart from three separate runs. After 10 minutes of radiation with black body night sky radiation the wavelength of 17.44μm is emitted; 5 minutes later at 15 minutes 17.57μm is emitted and so forth. Think of each of the spectral wavelengths as being a narrowband color wavelength. The first wavelength (see Table 5, Chapter 13) detected would be like a violet light (16-91μm) being turned on at 0 minutes, 5 minutes later (and so many yards closer to the female) a blue light (17.22μm) comes on, then a green (17.44μm), yellow (17.57μm), orange (17.64μm) and finally a red light (18.03μm) telling the male he had arrived. Since these frequencies are infrared frequencies we will of course have to give them different names than the names given color frequencies in the visible region. These infrared "color lights" tell the male exactly how far he is from the female.

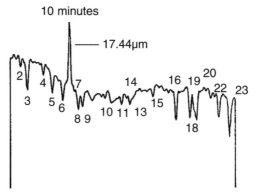

Figure 17. Narrow band maser-like infrared wavelength emitted from a thin layer of pheromone coated on a beeswax plate and rubbed with a silk cloth. The spectrum was taken after 10 minutes of radiation with black body night light. The numbered lines going downwards are the water vapor absorption lines in the region. This 10 minute 17.44µm wavelength emits between water vapor absorption line nos. 6 & 7. Each water line is numbered in this 17µm spectral region.

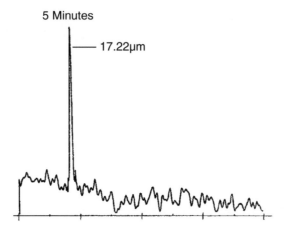

Figure 18. Narrow band maser-like line emitted after 5 minutes from a thin layer of pheromone coated on a beeswax plate, rubbed with a silk cloth, and modulated at 55 cps by vibrating the plate at that frequency. The moth both rubs and vibrates the antenna while searching the environment for scents. Note that the wavelength at 17.22 is much higher than that of the wavelength emitted if the pheromone is rubbed, but not modulated as was done at 10 minutes for the 17.44 wavelength. The modulated 17.22µm wavelength is so strong here that the water absorption lines are ratioed down and do not show up.

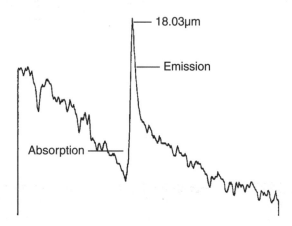

Figure 19. The pheromone gas in a salt cell radiated with an infrared black body $^{1}/_{1,000,000}$ second flash from an Edgerton strobe light. The gas pheromone absorbed considerable energy and then fluoresced a sharp peak at 18.03μm. The flash was set off after the pheromone had first been radiated for 25 minutes with normal night sky black body radiation so that the 18.03 wavelength at 25 minutes could be "pumped" by the higher black body energy from the strobe light. "Pumping" is the first process in getting high fluorescence out of the molecule so that it can be lased, or mased, as I call it. In these *gas cell* experiments the wavelengths are the opposite of those in nature where the concentration decreases with time (see text and *Figure 20*).

A Blueprint for Insect Control

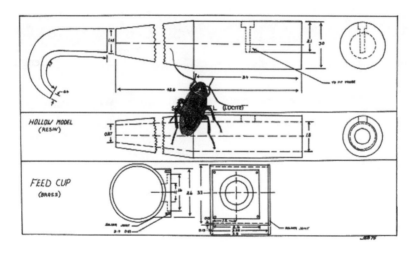

Chapter 11

A Blueprint for Insect Control

The great French mathematician Henri Poincare has written, "Originality of the human mind is not making up new configurations by arbitrary rearrangement of the myriad of known facts and concepts, but *discerning* among the nearly infinite number of possibilities those few combinations that are especially meaningful, useful or beautiful."

Poincare's words apply to all fields of human creative endeavor, and one can discern easily his exact meaning, for it is the same yardstick that a truly dedicated naturalist applies to his analysis of all observed behavioral phenomena.

The log-periodic infrared maser-like frequencies that I predicted, occur in a region of the infrared spectrum where there are a series of very weak water vibration-rotation absorption lines. At Honeywell Corporation in Minneapolis, we were able to purge the newer model interferometer system to eliminate water vapor and, consequently, the weak water-rotation lines in the 17- and 26-μm regions. When we eliminated the water vapor, the pheromone no longer emitted. In short, as in the case of almost all lasers, the system works only with a mixture of two gases — the pheromone plus water vapor. It apparently requires very little water vapor to trigger the stimulated emission.

Around 1963, laser physicists found that intense fluorescence — the basis of laser action — occurs in solutions of many organic compounds. Working with organic dyes that fluoresce in the visible region, they developed a tunable organic-dye laser. By mixing small amounts of the dye in a solvent, physicists discovered they could change the laser frequencies over a range of frequencies by changing the concentration of dye in the solvent. They named this phenomenon "concentration tuning."

It is a well-known fact that no liquid laser works as a pure molecular configuration and, actually, neither do solid-state, or gas lasers. The helium-neon laser is a mixture of two gases, and the ruby-red laser works because of the chrome-trace impurities in the ruby crystal.

The cabbage looper pheromone is a fleeting-floating mixture for, as I demonstrated, the pheromone works as a trace impurity in a "solvent" — in this case, the water vapor in the air. The water vapor reacts with the pheromone to produce its 17- and 26-micrometer fluorescence. In chemical terms, the interaction of water vapor and pheromone probably results from a resonance enhanced energy transfer between the pheromone and water vapor. As I pointed out in Chapter 3 on tuned circuits, this may be due (as in the case of a helium-neon laser) to "collisions" between the molecules of dissimilar gases.

The only difference between a contained organic-dye laser and the pheromone maser is that since the pheromone is free-floating, it changes in concentration as it floats farther and farther away from the emitting female where the concentration is greatest. In an organic-dye laser, the operator has to physically change the concentration to shift frequency by adding more of the dye.

In organic-dye lasers the molecules oscillate at longer wavelengths as the concentration increases. The same phenomenon holds for the fleeting-floating pheromone molecule; thus the cabbage looper male will "see" the shifting frequency at longer wavelengths close to the female, where the concentration is greatest, and at shorter and shorter wavelengths the farther away from the female when he begins his flight. This is a very elegant proximity indicator that tells the male exactly how far he has to travel to find the female. (see *Figure 20*).

As the pheromone concentration builds up on the antenna sensilla, and the thin layers get thicker and thicker, the system will eventually cut off. An enzyme secreted from the sensilla operates to break down and change the pheromone so that the insect can clean the antenna to begin again in an hour or so if he does not find a female. This is signal cut-off based on the increased concentration of the pheromone on the sensilla.

It is clear that the "morphology" of the various mixtures of the attractant is as important as the morphology of the sensilla sensors. Although few organic chemists would be willing to admit that they are "morphologists," that is exactly what they are. Physical chemists are "behaviorists," for they study the electromagnetic "behavior" of the molecule.

Wavengths (18 to 16μm)

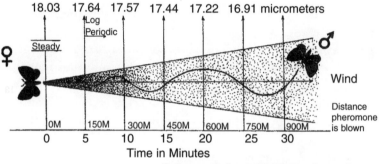

Figure 20. A male cabbage looper moth flying against an optimum wind speed of 0.5 meter/second detects the shortest wavelength (16.91μm) between 750 and 900 meters away. At that wind speed the frequency shifts to longer and longer wavelengths every 150 meters. Each frequency is "collected" by different groups of gradually lengthening log-periodic sensilla trichodea. When the male reaches the female, a steady 18.03μm (highest concentration) indicates close proximity to the target. This is an extremely elegant system for the pheromone is not only a directional system, but also a proximity indicator.

The work of physicists with organic-dye lasers gives us considerable insight into frequency shifts of narrowband laser energies consequent upon the mixing of different proportions of organic molecules. We must apply this knowledge to our search for the fleeting-floating infrared maser-like emissions from insect scent molecules.

The experimental verification of my previous predictions with respect to maser-like characteristics of the free-floating infrared-emitting pheromone, demonstrates the evolutionary uniqueness of the insect pheromone communication system. My study of the morphology of insect sensors, as applied to the waveguide properties of the sensilla sensors, will open the way to a plotting of the complex mixtures, and often shifting IR maser-like fleeting-floating frequencies of insect scents — whether host-plant, or sex attractants. It should be possible by thorough studies of the arrangement and form of sensilla sensors to predict resonant modes, and thus locate maser-like frequencies from various insect scents. It might even be possible, with the assemblage of a unique group of entomologists, antenna engineers, physicists, and physical chemists — plus of course, the aid of morphologists — to physically produce these free-floating maser-like emissions with enough energy to attract or jam the insect communication system over great distances. This would require manipulating scents to get maximum "in-phase" radiation of the selected frequencies.

At present, all of my experimental data indicates that the sensilla sensors decode these IR frequencies as thin layers of the emitting pheromone, either coated on or, conversely, suspended in a static field (rubbing experiments) angstroms away from the sensilla. In either case, the pheromone-coated sensilla operate as antenna-waveguide systems.

The mechanism of resonance could not have been determined without a thorough knowledge of the morphology of the insect antenna. Those who study the physiology of sensory perception and start at the detector inside the receiver, without looking at the morphology of the antenna outside the receiver, are — so to speak — trying to learn how the car runs without lifting the hood. It is, after all, the molecule and the antenna that "drive" the system. Detection is the last part of the system. A total analysis requires that we look at the entire system, not just one part of it.

Can we, based on this work, succeed in duplicating these coded fleeting-floating infrared signals that tell the moth or other insect species where mate, or host-plant, is located in the field? It would seem a rather difficult and "way out" thing to attempt, but I think most readers will agree that even finding these nebulous, maser-like log-periodic frequencies, was rather "way out." I have been told by more than one scientist that such strange maser-like frequencies could not occur from insect sex scents because such a phenomenon does not fit their ideas of how the molecule operates.

I found the frequencies not because I am a chemist; I found them for precisely the reason that I took an approach other than a strictly chemical one to the functioning of the insect antenna. It has taken me twenty years to prove that the insect antenna really is an antenna.

All of my measurements were based on the science of morphology — a science that insect physiologists seem to believe means little. To my knowledge, as of this writing, not a single physiologist has even commented on the form and sculpturing of the insect sensilla as it relates to an olfactory sensory system, theoretical or otherwise. On the other hand, I could not have decoded the system without the advice of innumerable electrical engineers and physicists who recognize, as I do, that form and frequency go together. It was the science of waveguide physics and electrical engineering that gave meaning to my studies of insect antenna form.

Up to this point I have used the terms antenna and waveguide as meaning the same thing. In a general way, they do mean the same thing. An antenna is a waveguide because it collects electromagnetic energy and guides it to the receiver. In electronic terms, however, they do have slightly different meanings.

For the purpose of arguing that the insect antenna is truly an electromagnetic organ, the distinction between the two systems is not important. If electromagnetic energy from a scent molecule couples from across space, then the sensilla is properly termed an antenna. It is immaterial if the separating gap is measured in meters, millimeters or micrometers. If the molecule is in direct contact with the surface of the sensilla, then the sensilla can quite properly be termed a waveguide. An antenna is not a detector and should not be thought of in that sense, although in my mind the detector system of the insect sensilla is built into the antennal system. The mechanism of detection, however, involves biological organic solid-state physics, and is the subject matter of an entirely different study.

The insect antenna-waveguide is a receiving antenna but, as I pointed out before, anything that makes a good receiving antenna also makes a good transmitting antenna. This is called the reciprocal law. The blueprint drawing at the beginning of the chapter shows an actual dielectric waveguide antenna modeled after a trichodea sensillum on the antenna of a noctuid moth. It was modeled by Dr. Paul Griffith while he was working on his doctoral dissertation at the Electronic Research Center at the University of California. He modeled it to measurements of the trichodea sensilla. It is made from hollow Lucite, a good dielectric, and curved at the tip — as are some of the sensilla on the corn earworm and cabbage looper antennae. It resonates in the millimeter-microwave region. When Griffith tested the antenna characteristics of this insect spine model, he found it to have very high "gain," both as a receiving and a transmitting antenna. (Gain is the term antenna engineers use to describe the efficiency of transmitting or receiving antennas.)

Of course this millimeter-long waveguide-antenna is much larger than the insect micrometer sensilla spines, but scaling is one very good method of telling us whether or not a system will work. This large-scale working model of the insect dielectric waveguide-antenna tells us that if we can miniaturize antennae down to micrometer size, we can produce artificial insect receiving and transmitting antennae. It is just as valid for us to use large-scale working models of tiny antenna systems as it is for the aeronautical engineers to build small working aerodynamic models of large aircraft to test in their wind tunnels. Model scaling is a technique used by engineers in all realms of technology.

Today, we can fashion transistors on a semiconductor chip that are one micron in size and we can make microlasers that are only 8 microns in length. These microlasers are virtually identical in size and shape to insect sensillae. These artificial "insect sensillae" lack the function of their biological counterparts, but their physical characteristics remain similar. Even though technology has come to the point where metal points can be fashioned and made by lasers, we do not have the capability of creating the biology, such as tissues and microtubules, that contribute to the working of an insect sensilla. Back in 1947, 4,000 electronic circuits utilizing vacuum tubes would take up a building as big as the radio range transmitter building that I helped install on O Shima Island in that year. Fortunately, in the last 50 years, we have developed the technological skills to miniaturize these antennae.

A bigger problem than the miniaturization of such tiny antennae would be the coupling of the energy from the tiny molecular oscillator to the tiny antenna. In order to accomplish the coupling of the energy from the molecular oscillator, the emission would have to be made coherent. In the case of the 17-µm log-periodic radiation, it is accomplished by the electret charge on the sensilla, which lines the molecules up like ranks of soldiers along the spine. The thermoelectret wax layer and rubbed charge accomplish the alignment, so that the 17- and 26-micrometer fluorescence is very narrowband and maser-like, as I have demonstrated.

The first spectrum in the figures at the end of Chapter 10 (*Figure 16*) shows log-periodic fluorescing 17µm radiation unmodulated, and detected by my Fourier transform infrared system at five minute intervals. The movement of the frequency from 16.91 to 18.03µm is obvious (see Table 5, Chapter 13). These spectrums were taken in a closed cell so that the concentration of evaporating scent increased with time because the scent was contained. In the field, the concentration would decrease as the pheromone floated away so that the wavelengths would be the reverse of those illustrated here (*Figure 20*). The next spectrum (*Figure 17*) shows the same fluorescence modulated. It is much stronger and easily detectable. The third spectrum shows a thin layer of the pheromone on a mirror. It has been rubbed slightly with a silk cloth and modulated. Note that like laser radiation it is extremely narrowband (*Figure 18*).

The last spectrum in the group (*Figure 19*) shows the results of my twenty-five years of research on insect antennae. The pheromone has been coated as a monolayer on a beeswax-coated plate, with a cabbage looper moth mounted beside the plate. When I stimulated the moth to fly by raising its legs from its perch, it flapped its wings against the plate so that the plate vibrated at exactly the same 50 cps as did the moth itself. During these vibrations, I utilized a high-speed ($1/1,000,000$ of a second) Edgerton flash to direct "pumping" energy into the pheromone on the plate. The high-speed Edgerton strobe light is used to take photographs of fast-traveling objects like bullets fired from a gun. Since it gives off considerable visible light, as well as lots of black body infrared light, I filtered out the visible light. Too much visible light causes the pheromone to absorb the visible radiation and not emit the IR 17-µm fluorescence. Note that the pheromone 17-µm signal is extremely high and extremely narrowband at the top of the rising spectral line. In short, I partially "lased" the actual insect cabbage looper pheromone. I not only have "tuned in to nature," but have "lased nature" as well.

Of course this is another paradoxical statement, for man has been "lasing nature" all along. The reason the pheromone used in conjunction with a black light trap increases the moth catch six to ten times, is that the black body "pumping" radiation from the BL bulb is extremely high, consequently the pheromone puts out a much stronger signal near the light trap than it does away from the light trap where the lower-energy, natural night-sky radiation pumps the pheromone instead.

The beauty of the system is summarized in *Figure 20*. The moth flies the maser-like emissions from the pheromone just as I used to fly a radio range during World War II. It flies in and out of the luminous stream of molecules along the strongest IR signal. Now you should know why I said that Laithwaite and Kettlewell were both right. Kettlewell was right because it was scent; Laithwaite was right because it was IR radiation. Laithwaite must have been very wrong about his moths flying with the wind, as was Jean Henri Fabre, for the wind must carry the little emitting satellites to the antenna.

The pheromone signal is much better than my old radio range transmitter, because it tells the flying male moth how far he is from the pheromone-releasing female.

According to Dr. Harry Shorey, who has studied the cabbage looper pheromone in the field, the signal works best at the wind speed of 0.5 meters/second. The pheromone traveling away from the female at that speed would travel 150 meters every five minutes. Since the pheromone moves from frequency to frequency periodically, as the concentration decreases with distance, the moth at any period is utilizing a different group of his log-periodically arranged sensilla to "catch" the IR maser-like signals. In this free-floating organic maser-like system, the longest wavelength at 18.03 micrometers occurs right at the female, because it is there that the concentration is highest. The shorter wavelength at 16.91 micrometers would occur 900 meters away, assuming a wind speed of 0.5 meters/second. That is a little more than half a mile or almost one kilometer. Another beautiful feature of the system is that the male moth can adjust his flight speed to the wind speed to fly the IR luminous beam at maximum efficiency. He can also use his vibration-sensing Johnston's organ to set his antenna vibratory frequency for the proper antennae vibrations at 50 to 55 cps to modulate the emitted signal.

Certainly if I, a biologist with scant training in chemistry, could decode this complex infrared maser-like communication system, then a team of competent antenna-waveguide scientists and solid-state physicists, working with physical chemists, could design and produce an efficient 17-micrometer-emitting solid-state sandwich oscillator utilizing the organic pheromone itself (see Epilogue).

Paul Griffith used a cup-like base to couple the energy from his millimeter microwave system to his model antenna. It was a very difficult coupling problem, but he did get the microwave oscillations to the dielectric antenna from which they were transmitted.

I am working at lasing the pheromone so I can use it directly as the frequency oscillator. But the problem of producing the microminiature antenna, and then coupling the energy into the little rods so that they throw out the frequencies in phase, is a production problem best solved by companies that specialize in miniaturized integrated circuits.

The usefulness of such a miniature frequency system is obvious. The farmer, instead of going to the store to buy a bag of insecticide, will buy, or lease, a little microminiature transmitter that either attracts the insect species attacking his corn or cabbage plants or, conversely, beats against the insect pheromone frequency and jams it so that mating does not take place. Therefore, no mating, resulting in only unfertilized eggs oviposited on his cabbage.

Each year he will probably have to replace the batteries in his transmitter — much cheaper than buying sacks of dangerous chemicals. As for the old bug-a-boo that such a system puts all the insecticide companies out of business — I can only ask, why? Could not the same companies that produce insecticides produce the chemicals to make the little solid-state transmitters, and perhaps even the transmitters themselves? We are, after all, talking about a chemical solid-state transmitter. The same farmer supply retail stores that now sell and service insecticide systems could just as effectively sell and service the little transmitter systems. I am afraid that too many American businessmen, who constantly preach free enterprise, have forgotten that the greatness of this country comes from innovative technological advancements in a free political society. Surely an improvement in methods of insect control, if they contribute to saving the environment, are to be preferred to an outdated, dangerous and archaic system of pest eradication. Perhaps it is sad but true, that far too many leaders in our country would rather "fight than switch."

Infrared frequencies are the natural frequencies in which we are bathed all our lives. Inasmuch as the attractant or jamming frequencies would be narrowband, they would be of extremely low energy. In fact, the radiated molecules from innumerable scents floating under your local mercury-vapor street lamps are, no doubt, putting out hundreds of such frequencies at every street corner in America. It is these lamp-radiated scent molecules that attract and confuse so many night-flying insects swarming around in the radiated vapors under the lamp.

There is one final practical advantage to such an insect control device, in addition to its ability to attract only the selected species to which it is tuned: it can be turned off when not in use. That is precisely what is wrong with insecticides — they cannot be turned off.

My Friend the Nettle

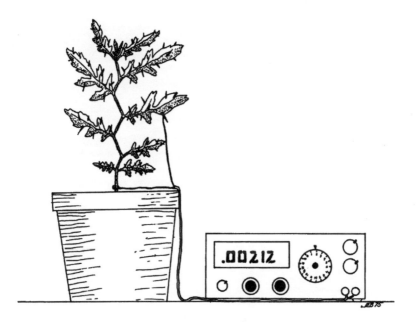

Chapter 12
My Friend the Nettle

Let us consider for a moment that insects are not the only living organisms with spines. Plants are also covered with spines called *trichomes* by botanists, from the Greek root *trich* meaning *hair*. In almost all cases they are tapered. As with insects, the outer covering of plants is called a cuticle. The insect and plant cuticles have a lot in common. For one thing, they are both coated with a thin layer of wax. Plant waxes, like insect waxes, are excellent thermoelectrets, and they also have *piezoelectric* (pressure-detection) and *pyroelectric* (radiation-detection) capabilities.

Without going into all the details of plant electrets, for this is a book on insects, I need only point out and emphasize again that environmental parameters — humidity, temperature, light, infrared radiation, air ions and pressure — affect the electret properties of wax, and that waxes (plant or insect types) can be utilized, in one configuration or another, to detect or control these environmental factors.

Robert Hook, the developer of the compound microscope, was the first researcher to study in detail the surface of the leaf. Hook, an astute naturalist, studied the hair on the leaves of the common nettle, *Urtica dioica*.

The hairs on the leaves and stems of plants are generally micrometers in length, but consider also the thorns on cacti: they are usually measured in millimeters. The sun not only gives off infrared radiation in the micrometer wavelength region, but the millimeter as well. These latter frequencies lie in the microwave region. Dr. G. C. Southworth first discovered this microwave radiation from the sun in 1942, while working at a Bell Telephone laboratory.

The spines of cacti are modified leaves, and thus intimately tied up with water balance in the plant. They have one function, dependent on their waxy cuticle, but this does not mean that they might not have a second function based on form, arrangement, length and diameter of the spines. The shape, size and arrangement of these cacti spines are as numerous as the species themselves. Botanists have shown that trichomes have a cuticle, but generally they have associated its function with water balance, as have the insect physiologists. This is a true function of both the plant and insect cuticles, but to ignore the form of these elegant plant hairs is to commit the entomologist's sin of omission. The plant taxonomists and morphologists contributed the most significant data on plant hairs. Without the work of these research gentlemen this book could not have been written, for they are the best observers of nature's details.

Some of the elegant forms of plant hairs are shown in my plate of six common plant families (see *Figure 21*). The hairs were copied from the *Anatomy of the Dicotyledons* by C.R. Metcalfe & L. Chalk (1950). These researchers point out that entire plant families can be identified by the occurrence of one or more distinctive shapes of hairs. In other cases they can identify genera and species within a family group by the hairs. The real clue to the function of trichomes, however, is in my opinion contained in the statement that, "the length, size, and density of hairs are more liable to *vary* with *environment* than in the occurrence of different kinds, so that the former features are of more restricted taxonomic value." In that sentence it is not difficult for a thoughtful mind to change length to length divided by wavelengths (wavelength criteria), size into diameter, and population density to array. What these gentlemen have learned from their study of the morphology of plant surfaces is that, although families generally have certain types (forms) of hairs in common, the species and genera within a family have different arrangements (arrays), sizes and lengths of their hairs that vary with the environment where the plant grows. If this is so, and the drawings of hairs in their two volumes suggest that it is, then the connection between hair length, size and arrangement,

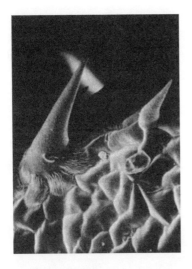

(*Above left*) Trichomes along the leaf of a cranesbill weed (Geranium family). Note the extreme tapered configuration. The leaf-edge trichomes are common on many plants. Botanists have no really good explanation of the function of trichomes. They may be excellent models for solar energy collectors. Cranesbill is the first early spring host plant in Florida of the corn earworm moths, which later in the season lays its eggs on sweet corn and cotton. (*Above right*) Curved trichomes (spines) on the dorsal surface of the small veins of a wild grape leaf. These plant spines are hollow, and are also coated with a thin layer of wax as are the sensilla spines on insect antennae.

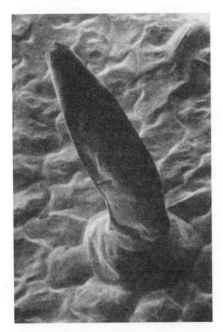

(*Left*) Thin-walled trichome on the dorsal surface of a tomato plant leaf. Some trichomes are glandular and produce liquid substances from their tips. This trichome, and that of the grape and cranesbill, are hollow. Either type, however, hollow or liquid-filled, could function as a dielectric waveguide for collecting and controlling energy from the electromagnetic output of the sun.

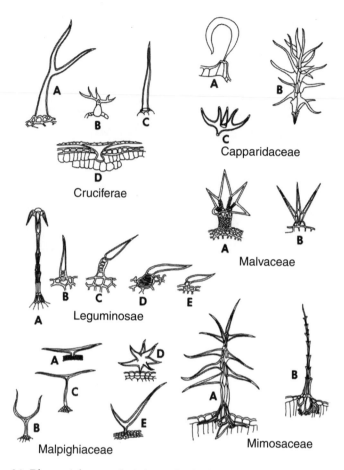

Figure 21. Plant trichomes (hairs) on the leaf surface of certain plants in six different families. (From *Anatomy of the Dicotyledones*, by C. R. Metcalfe and L. Chalk (1950).)

Cruciferae: A. *Hesperis glutinosa*, B. *Matthiola livida*, C. *Capsella bursa-pastoris*, D. *Cheiranthus cheiri*.

Capparidaceae: A *Capparis Spinosa*, B *Capparis domingensis*, C. *Capparis zeylanica*.

Leguminosae: A *Cranocarpus martii*, B., C., D., E. Simple hairs of Leguminosae.

Malvaceae: A. Stellate hair of *Malvastrum asperrimum*, B. Stellate hair of *Malachra radiata*.

Malpighiaceae: A. *Malpighia urens*, B. & C. *Perixotoa macrophylla*, D. *Thryallis brachystachys*, E. *Mascagnia cordifolia*.

Mimosaceae: A. Shaggy hair of *Mimosa furfuracea*, B. Shaggy hair of *Mimosa obtusifolia*.

and the environment is either an unlikely coincidence, or these plant trichomes are waveguide-antenna control systems utilized by the plant to "program" each species to its specific environment.

We know from the studies of plant physiologists that plants are carefully controlled by their environment. One need only read John Ott's delightful book, *My Ivory Cellar,* to get a subtle feeling for the precise environmental control of plants.

Cacti dwell in a very restricted and harsh environment, and are certainly dependent on maximum utilization of the surrounding biosphere. The spines of cacti and the hairs on leaves may well be open resonators, many wavelengths long, in the visible, infrared, or microwave region of the spectrum. If so, the leaves of plants and "spine-like" leaves of cacti are tuned by means of these projections into the sun and perhaps, in some cases, even into the moon or stars, which also give off innumerable subtle visible, infrared and microwave lines.

Scientists who study photoperiodism and daily rhythms in living organisms, speak about biological clocks and timing mechanisms. Generally there are two schools of thought as to how these daily life rhythms are timed. One school says that the mechanism of control is endogenous, which means the timing mechanism originates within the body. The other school considers all such timing mechanisms as being exogenous, which means that the timing mechanism originates from without; in other words, the timing signal comes from the surrounding environment. There are extremes of belief in one or the other of these two schools of thought, but in general both types of timing control appear to exist side by side in all living organisms. That is exactly what makes the mechanism of rhythmic phenomenon so difficult to decode. It is easy, for instance, to show that various amounts of light (daylight) affect the flowering of plants or the migration of birds. The difficulty lies in showing what the exact control frequencies are, and how they work within the organism to program the life cycle.

Scientists who study photoperiodism in living organisms are more likely to belong to the exogenous school, since they are able to affect the behavior of plants and animals by manipulating the amount and spectral content of light that reaches the organism.

As early as 1948, a group of USDA scientists under the leadership of H. A. Borthwick and S. B. Hendricks began studies on the photoperiodic control of flowering in plants. They discovered that red and far-red light (visible red that is almost into the infrared region of the spectrum) regulate many of the plant-growth processes. They isolated a protein molecule called phytochrome, which operates as the control light switch in plants. Their studies demonstrated that phytochrome responds to the light and governs stem growth, flowering, germination and other life processes. The molecule may be likened to an "on-off" switch, for it operates in both an active and an inactive form. When phytochrome is active, exposure to far-red light converts it to the inactive form; when it is inactive, exposure to regular red light (shorter wavelength than far-red) converts it to the active form. The switch that activates or deactivates phytochrome is a light-absorbing pigment (related to human bile) that constitutes only one percent of the phytochrome molecule. The pigment is called chromophore from the Greek *chromo* for color and *phoros* meaning to carry. The chemical, chromophore, is a color carrier. Reduced to its simplified meaning, color is a frequency, and anything that absorbs (receives) or transmits a frequency — even a pigment — is an antenna.

One of the real failures of twentieth century science is that, with the introduction of quantum theory, physicists — and in particular, biologists — neglected classical waveguide theory based on the elegant work of Maxwell and his waveguide equations. They have concentrated almost entirely on quantum analysis of light-absorption phenomena by pigments and other molecules. With the invention of the laser, scientists have come to realize that the classical waveguide-resonator theory has much to tell us about how molecular resonating systems work. In science, as in agriculture, it is not good to put all your eggs in one basket. I believe that the double helix of DNA is certainly a pair of helical antennae, transmitting and receiving over angstroms (1 angstrom = 1 ten-billionth of a meter) instead of over meters, or kilometers. The difference in distance is of no consequence to principle. A walky-talky transmitting a few blocks is as much a waveguide resonating system as is the transmitter that sent back photographs of Mars from over 39 million miles away. Resonant systems are resonant systems, and it is time more scientists went back to the end of the nineteenth century — the real renaissance of science — and reexamined some of the elegant classical waveguide theories of that period in the light of what we know today.

Not only has classical nineteenth century theory been neglected, but so also have been the researchers who accomplished the work. Botany has its own forgotten genius — Jagadis Chandra Bose. He was born November 3, 1858, and educated at St. Xavier's College in Calcutta, India. He graduated with high honors from Cambridge University in 1884. Bose served as Professor of Physical Science at Presidency College, Calcutta, between 1885 and 1915, and later founded and directed the Bose Research Institute in that same city from 1917 to 1937. He died in Giridih, Bengal on November 3, 1937.

Bose was as much a plant physiologist as he was a physicist. In other words he was what I call a generalist, or first-rate naturalist. I need not go into details of the life of this fascinating man, for it is well documented in that intriguing work, *The Secret Life of Plants*, by Peter Tompkins and Christopher Bird.

As a physicist, Bose made significant contributions to our knowledge of electromagnetic radiation by verifying the laws of reflection, refraction and polarization of electric waves. His work in the field of plant physiology was fifty years ahead of its time: he built sensitive machines for measuring the movement and growth of plants, he succeeded, with his sensitive apparatus in defining the effects of sleep, air, drugs and nutrients on plants, and he categorically proved a unifying parallelism between the responses of plants and animals to the environment. Between 1902 and 1929, Bose published nine books covering his research on the "awareness" of plants to their environment.

One of Bose's most important researches appeared in the 1914 *Annual Report* of the Smithsonian Institution (pp. 421-443). It is entitled "Plant Autographs and Their Revelations." The paper describes in detail the ingenious resonant recorder that he developed to study plant movement in mimosa plants.

Bose's autograph machine produced a record of microscopic plant movement around the 24-hour cycle. It is easy to visualize that if a plant makes subtle movement in a repeatable cyclic sequence, then there must also be electrical effects occurring at the same time. Current, in such a "system," would be expected to peak at the peaks of the movements.

I set out with my own sensitive instrument (a solid-state Pico-electrometer) to record current along the length of a plant antenna (spine). The subject of my eight-week preliminary experiments was a common southern nettle of the genus *Solanum*. It was chosen because of the elegance and shape of its regularly spaced spines, which average 2 mm in length.

Figure 22 (*top*) demonstrates that the current along the antenna spine did indeed vary over a 24-hour cycle, in direct agreement with Bose's (*bottom*) recording of movement, as shown by the dip during the dark hours (7:00 p.m. to 7:00 a.m., EST, Spring). The only observable difference between the movement curve of Bose — which I smoothed out — and my current curve, is that the mimosa shows a slight peak at dusk; this does not occur in my current recording for cloudy days (average of six days). The sunny-day recordings (average of twenty days) show a three-peak oscillation with maximums at 12:30 p.m. (noon), 3:00 p.m., and 6:30 p.m. (sunset). Interestingly, there are continual low-amplitude oscillations throughout the day, whether cloudy or bright. On cloudy days the current is slightly higher than it is on sunny days. At night there are no oscillations, and the decrease in current is accompanied by high-amplitude oscillations at dusk and dawn (sunny recording), followed by the straight line (sleep?). On the three days when Gainesville had its usual late afternoon thunder showers, the dawn and dusk oscillations did not occur. Furthermore, the quiescent period of "sleep" was delayed, and the huge amounts of static electricity from lightning caused the current to vary tremendously. After the storm, the resting period was interrupted by equally spaced (every twenty minutes) "nightmares" — or perhaps "dreams" would be a better term.

We see, then, that by coupling into a single spine on a nettle plant, the plant's electrical "life cycle" can easily be followed. With a sensitive modern-day solid-state Pico electrometer, which can read down to 10-13 picoamps (one trillionth of an amp), it is fairly easy to accomplish such recordings.

A lie detector was utilized by Cleve Backster, who is amply quoted in Tompkins and Bird's *The Secret Life of Plants*, in order to study the sensitivity of plants. A lie detector is a fairly insensitive instrument designed to measure human electrical responses. Solid-state electronic developments have given us more sensitive instruments.

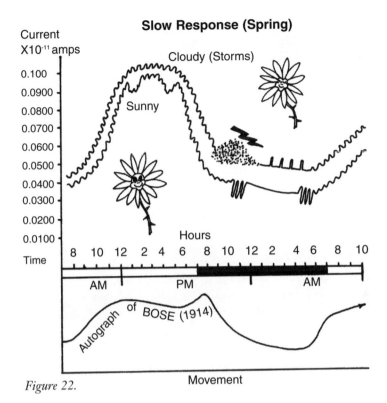

Figure 22.

My friend, the nettle, can easily detect a person approaching. Because the wax-coated outer layer of the spine is an electret, it is highly sensitive to static charges. Clothing styles from the 70s cause the same burst of static disruptions as does lightning. The reason for this is that we wore synthetic fabrics containing nylon and polyester. A re-emergence of these clothing styles appeared twenty years later (I *never* imagined that bell-bottoms would return), but in order to get a true reading of the plant as a "person sensor," one must approach the plant in cotton clothing or, better yet, no clothing. This makes one wonder about the effects of dielectric static generators — such as polyesters and nylon — which cover some of us throughout most of the day.

Strangely enough, after the plant has been sensitized by a lightning storm, or even by a simulated lightening storm, such as by a high-frequency Tesla coil, or even by a piece of nylon rubbed vigorously near the spine, the plant responds with increased sensitivity (current increases) to a candle (visible or infrared radiation) and also to sound.

The response to sound causes us to believe that there is no reason not to conclude that plants respond to music, as demonstrated in the elegant experiments of Dorothy Retallack (*The Sound of Music and Plants*). The fact that Mrs. Retallack had to publish her work in book form because scientific journals would not accept it, is certainly no condemnation of her carefully controlled experiments. Rather, it is a condemnation of the anonymous peer-review system of so-called "objective" scientific journals which consistently reject works that do not fit, or that contradict the sanctified paradigms of the ruling clique of scientists.

I may state, with almost absolute certainty, that in some journals a review of this book will point out that my preliminary experiments on plants (not to mention insects) simply cannot be. The entire criticism will revolve around the fact that I use the words: sleep, sense, and movement, as did Bose in his research. In short, the criticism will not stand on facts or the repeatability of my experiments, nor upon the known dielectric and electret properties of wax, but rather on the semantics of words. In short, again, I shall be accused of that most dreadful of all scientific sins: anthropomorphism. Personally, I see no reason why the quiescent period of a plant should not be called sleep, any more than that of a fish, mammal or insect.

In 1914, Bose wrote, "Is the plant equally excitable throughout the day or night? If not, is there any particular period at which the excitability remains uniform? Is there, again, a different time during which the plant loses its sensibility — going, as it were, to sleep?" He heads his paragraphs on the diurnal excitability of plants, "The Sleep of Plants." For that mortal sin, his facts have been ignored for more than eighty-five years.

Bose maintained that plants, in fact, have a nervous system, and I agree with his thesis, for if we are to consider the wax-coated spines of an insect a part of the lower animal's nervous system, then there is no justifiable reason not to consider the wax-coated spines of plants a part of the plant nervous system. There is a certain unity in all of nature that cannot be denied, and I am enough of a romantic — some would say a mystic — to believe that such unity pervades the living spirit of all organic matter. I would like the physicist-botanist, Professor Bose, to help clarify this subject because he said it far better than I could:

> We have now before our mind's eye the whole organism of the perceiving, throbbing, and responding plant, a complex unity and not a congeries of unrelated parts. The barriers which separated kindred phenomena in the plant and animal are now thrown down. This community throughout the great ocean of life is seen to outweigh apparent dissimilarity. Diversity is swallowed up in unity. In realizing this, is our sense of final mystery of things deepened or lessened? Is our sense of wonder diminished when we realize in the infinite expanse of life that is silent and voiceless, the foreshadowing of more wonderful complexities? Is this not rather that science evokes in us a deeper sense of awe? Does not each of her new advances gain for us a step in that stairway of rock which all must climb who desire to look from the mountain top of the spirit upon the promised land of truth?

Along with Professor Bose, I believe that truth is truth, regardless of the size of the words used to describe it, and if the mass of humankind — specialists included — want to believe that plants have "feelings," then that is reasonable enough for me. Plants sense the environment with their antennae, and that is exactly what the word "feel" means.

An Epilogue:
An Infrared Emission
Insect Trap

Chapter 13

An Epilogue:
An Infrared Emission Insect Trap

In his interesting two volumes, *Savage Life* and *Scenes in Australia* (1847), G. F. Angas writes that the Australian aborigines feasted on large ghost moths, *Trictena argentata*, that fluttered into the hot embers of their campfire on the banks of the Lower Murray River. The moths were essentially self-cooked, and the natives popped the scorched and roasted moth bodies into their mouths directly from the embers.

Surrounded by, and deep within, the tree-shrouded night jungles of northern Luzon, I have watched negrito pygmies feast on the night-flying moths that are lured recklessly into glowing fires built to attract them. The negritos seem to sense the exact time when these moth denizens-of-the-dark will emerge from their pupal cases.

Anyone who knows the least thing about jungle survival builds green-wood fires for jungle camping. For one thing, the thick smoke keeps mosquitoes away, and for another, green wood makes very hot and excellent cooking embers that last a long time. The continual crackling and popping of sap-filled green wood also keeps jungle animals at a distance for those who do not like their sleep disturbed by the pitter-patter of curious wild life.

In American campgrounds, fires are built of dry wood that is usually used for warmth or light; one seldom sees moths flying into them. The green-wood fire, however, is another phenomenon entirely, for above such a fire is the swirling and heated mass of hydrocarbons squeezed from the green wood by the intense heat. The jungle natives know the best type of attractant fire to lure the moth bridegroom to his fate. It would take a hundred Fourier transform interferometers in a row to begin to study all of the thousands of infrared frequencies that are emitted from the heated hydrocarbon gases above a green-ember fire. I once calculated that if we allowed one narrowband frequency line for each of the many band widths that will fit within the atmospheric windows between 2 and 30 micrometers, we would have more than 930 different emitting infrared "radio" stations. Since the infrared frequencies moths use are likely coded to more than one wavelength, the possibilities for selective species signals run into the millions. When one considers the millions of insect species that exist in nature, the beauty of such a frequency-coded scent system is obvious.

Scans of paraffin and beeswax candles show them to emit many, many narrowband IR frequencies between 2 and 30 micrometers. I have often seen the cabbage looper male protrude his claspers toward the flame — something he does only in the presence of his own species' pheromone. As I suspected, the candle flame emits almost exactly the same narrow 17-µm lines (Table 5) as the pheromone. The discovery of the 17-µm log-periodic maser-like frequencies from the pheromone, and also from a flickering candle, solved the candle mystery for me. No wonder the poor male is confused; they all come from the candle at the same time. The narrowband infrared emissions from a flickering candle between 6 and 30 micrometers are also shown in the Fourier spectrum beneath the candle drawing at the beginning of Chapter 8.

Strangely enough, not only are all of the 17-micrometer narrow maser-like pheromone lines present in the candle, but also the broad black body ILS signal described in Chapter 5. The candle, in a more or less crude way, mimics the moth body-wing modulated signal, because the flickering of the flame in the air modulates the candle black body radiation between 6 and 25 micrometers. Both the narrowband molecular signals from the pheromone, and the body-wing's modulated broadband IR body signal are inherent to a candle flame — these, as well as the fact that the visible and UV frequencies detectable by the moths' eyes are also present. When one considers the variety of all of these frequencies

Table 5

Comparison of the Log-Periodic IR Emission Lines of the Pheromone with the IR Emission Lines of a Wax Candle in the 17-μm Region

| | Wavelengths | |
Pheromone time in minutes	Pheromone (μm)	Candle* (μm)
0	16.95	16.91
5	17.21	17.22
10	17.39	17.44
15	17.57	17.57
20	17.73	17.64
25	17.95	17.95
30	18.12	18.03

*Although the candle emission wavelengths do not in every case match exactly the pheromone wavelengths, the candle is still an excellent radiation mimic of the pheromone, because the phenomenon is no different from having your radio receiver tuned slightly off the center of the wavelength. You can still hear the music, but not as efficiently, nor is it as loud.

working on the central nervous system of a moth at one time, the complexities of the insect communication system are, indeed, impressive. By a series of frequencies, the moth is, so to speak, "programmed" like an orbiting satellite to respond to certain environmental signals. As long as the moth is not "sick" — that is, his receiver and antennae out of order — he will respond to the signal regardless of the consequences. He plunges into the embers of the green-wood fire because his antenna-waveguide receiver has received a message that is a mimic of nature's natural programmed message. Once we have learned to build and program little solid-state transmitters to duplicate these very shortwave, narrowband IR "radio" stations, we shall be on our way to "tuning in" to insects for selective control and protection of our crop lands.

As I pointed out in Chapter 1, the candle in many ways resembles the sun. It gives off numerous narrowband visible and infrared emissions. If we can tune to a candle from across a few yards of space, we should be able to tune to the sun across millions of miles of space. To accomplish tuning in to the sun, we will without a doubt have to consider doing it with micrometer-long spines, or pits, in the same manner that plants and insects accomplish this.

Spine-like projections, considered as waveguides for collecting energy, have been thought about by other researchers. As mentioned before, there are numerous historical examples of researchers in various parts of the world having the same idea at the same time. The best example of this is the simultaneous American and Russian invention of the laser. My own work is also a good example of two researchers working on different projects, but with the same theoretical viewpoint: both of us were doing research on the same campus at the University of Florida, but we were totally unaware of one another.

Professor Robert Bailey, of the Electrical Engineering Department, had designed and produced a metal model of what he calls an Electromagnetic Wave Energy Converter (EWEC). In 1973, he obtained a patent through NASA for his EWEC (see *Figure 23*). The drawing from his patent, which is a design for one that works in the microwave portion of the spectrum, is very similar to the tapered insect dielectric spines. When Professor Bailey was told about my work by another researcher who had heard my seminar before a meeting of electrical engineers, he immediately recognized the similarity of the problems involved in our respective research fields. He crossed the campus — a distance of approximately one mile — to tell me about his work. As fate would have it, we were slightly closer together than were the American and Russian developers of the laser.

The EWEC was designed for the specific purpose of collecting the sun's electromagnetic energy and converting it directly into electricity for domestic use. This would, of course, save our fossil fuels for the manufacturing processes upon which our economy and the strength of our nation rest. For those who enjoy reading, remember how difficult it would be to manufacture this book without fossil fuels to produce paper.

Professor Bailey believes, as do I, that to efficiently tune in to the sun we must miniaturize his EWEC down to visible and infrared wavelengths where the greater portion of the sun's energy lies. This means utilizing dielectric materials, not metals, as dielectrics are the best resonators at these short wavelengths. We must design the EWEC as a dielectric antenna-collector of radiation.

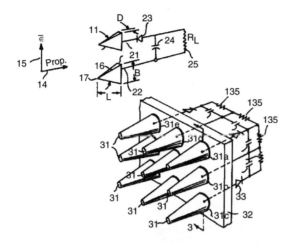

Figure 23. The Electromagnetic Wave Energy Converter (EWEC) created by Professor Robert Bailey of the Electrical Engineering Department of the University of Florida (U.S. Patent No. 3760257 September 18, 1973 NASA). This invention was in a very early stage of development. It resembles to a startling degree the dielectric wax-coated sensilla of the insect antenna.

The chief solar energy conversion technique that was under study for Earthbound use, was the silicon solar cell, an established technology created for the space program. Sunlight impinging upon these smooth-surfaced cells, causes electrons to flow, and thereby creates direct current (DC).

Solar cells presently have a conversion efficiency of about 15 percent. Thus, if 1,000 watts of sunlight fall upon one square meter (39" x 39") of solar cell material, the resulting DC output is 150 watts.

The EWEC promises some major advantages over solar cells. For example, early calculations show that the EWEC may have a theoretical conversion efficiency rate of about 50 to 70 percent. Mechanical flexibility appears inherent in the EWEC. If the absorber elements are mounted on a flexible substrate, while solar cells often crack and lose efficiency if not mounted on a flat surface, it may be possible, ultimately, to manufacture large-area, low-cost EWEC absorbers on a sheet-roll process — a feat of economy not formerly achieved with solar cells.

Professor Bailey and I began working quite closely together on his solar energy project. As in the case of my work, the biggest problem is not in miniaturizing the small collector spines, but rather in coupling in to the collected infrared energy, and converting it into electricity. From my observations of insects and plants, there is no doubt this can be done by copying nature.

If, as my experiments indicate, the hairs on the leaves of plants are really dielectric waveguide-antennae for collecting energy in the form of infrared or microwave signals from the sun, then Professor Bailey and I have excellent models in plants, as well as insects, for our solar energy research. (Remember that the sun has millions of narrowband radiating emissions in all portions of the spectrum.)

I am sure that by now my reader has arrived at the conclusion that I am infatuated with spines. That, of course, is true, and I am deeply suspicious of a researcher who is not infatuated with the elegance of nature, spines being a part of that elegance. Electromagnetic waves are as much a part of nature as are the insects and plants themselves. I have always been disappointed in Hertz, for whom the electromagnetic waves are named. He was not alone in the discovery of radio waves — Hughes deserves equal recognition — and Hertz once wrote to the Dresden Chamber of Commerce that all research into the characteristics of electromagnetic waves should be discouraged, because they could not be utilized to any good purpose. So be it.

It is possibly true that my dielectric spines cannot be put to any useful purpose, but if this is true, then why do insects and plants persist in growing the little micrometer hairs? If I "be fooled," then I admit to having lived for fifty years in a fool's paradise.

I have little use for "anonymous" peer reviews, for it is much more enlightening to be able to discuss one's research papers with one's peers. Anonymous peer reviews are a cover-up. Nevertheless, anonymous peer reviews of a paper can, at times, be delightfully provocative. The following accompanied the first rejection of my log-periodic emission paper:

> *I find this work either incredible or misleadingly described. The center of my objection is the idea that a log-periodic distribution of antenna component scale should be related to a time variation of emission frequency which takes place in a matter of minutes.* The whole idea of antenna log-periodic design implied here is quite contrary to my own. *I will not go on to*

discuss the maser or night sky light. Absent is some showing of causality; mere flow charts and analogy are inadequate. There is meat in this paper, but it is hidden beneath a panache of showy claims and interesting if uncertain analogies. If I am too harsh, another referee should be asked. But the author ought to re-examine his own views on how far a result should be hidden beneath a layer of speculation. [Emphasis is the author's.]

In my younger days I would have been upset or perhaps even angry at such a review, but anger only serves to dull the wits, and anger definitely obscures the humor of such a paragraph.

Here is the classic example of one scientist saying to another, "You can't publish this because I don't agree with you." Although he admits the findings are incredible, they still should not be published. Of course these findings are incredible, not because I discovered the pheromone emissions, but because nature is incredible. Where is the objectivity of science in this type of anonymous peer review? Statements such as those of the reviewer emphasize that objectivity does not reside in the scientist, but rather in a system of experimentation that demands that significant findings be repeatable in terms of the described experimental method. Because a finding is incredible, it does not mean that it is not real. The realities of nature are far more incredible than the wildest dreams. Once an unknown reality is manifested, it ceases to be a mystery, and thus it suffers a loss of glamour. To uncover an incredible reality requires imagination plus appropriate experimental action-not dreaming or wishing.

In their stimulating book, *The Morning of the Magicians*, Louis Pauwels and Jacques Bergier pinpoint the reality of the fantastic in one vivid paragraph:

Artists who seek for the fantastic outside reality in the clouds, lack imagination. *They return from their exploration with nothing more than counterfeits. As it is with rare minerals so with the fantastic; it has to be torn out of the very bowels of the Earth, from the heart of reality. True imagination is something other than a leap into the unreal. No other aspect of the mind dives so deeply as the imagination. The fantastic is usually thought of as a violation of natural law, as a rising up of the impossible. This is not how we conceive it. It is rather a*

A technician of the Special Electronic Branch of Sylvania Electric Company assembles a microwave log-periodic antenna. Note that each element is tapered and that the spacing gets closer and closer from the base to the tip. Such an antenna is broadband, and each segment "slides" smoothly from one frequency to another so that it covers a wide band of resonate frequencies. The sensilla of the cabbage lopper and corn earworm moth are arranged in just such a log-periodic fashion so that they resonate and "slide" from frequency to frequency emitted log-periodically from the sex pheromone (Chapter 10). It was by observing such manmade antennas that the author began treating insect antennae as, in reality, electromagnetic antennas. This is reverse bionics. (Photo courtesy of the Electronic Systems Group, GET, Sylvania Electric company.)

manifestation of natural law, an effect produced by contact with reality-reality perceived directly and not through a filter of habit, prejudice, conformism. [Emphasis is the author's.]

Scientists can be habitual, prejudiced and conformist, like any other group of individuals. In the vast majority of cases they are more so, for the very reason that most of them are trained as extremely narrow specialists. That is also why it is so necessary for a generalist to learn more than one scientific language, even though he can never learn it as well as the researcher "reared" in the subject matter. He is like the traveler with the handicap of near illiteracy stumbling around in a new land.

Scientists are seldom vindictive, but their logic can at times be obscure. The reviewer of my paper paid me a compliment when he described my work as "incredible. " It is so "incredible" that I must be misleading him — "pulling his leg," as the old Irish saying goes. He doesn't suggest that I didn't find these strange log-periodic frequencies, because he knows that I replicated the experiment 160 times. What he says is that the emissions have nothing to do with the log-periodic arrangement and dielectric properties of the spine sensilla. In other words, the forms of nature are meaningless. Spines are grown by plants and insects for the benefit of the taxonomists classifying the organisms, and have no real use in the secret life of the insect or plant. Actually this design of nature could be (one chance in several billion) a huge coincidence — a joke of fate on Callahan, so to speak. If it is, however, I wish that the Sylvania Corporation would have stopped reinforcing my illusions by constructing tapered microwave log-periodic antennas that work in the millimeter region.

What I have passed on to you in this book comes from my intellect, but just as important, it comes from the heart. The heart can often lead one astray. The fact remains, however, that a researcher whose heart is not in his work is no researcher at all.

Because I enjoyed my job, I worked hard at it. In fact, I may be busier now since my retirement in 1986. But no matter how hard a single person works, he or she is not likely to solve any of the problems of this spaceship Earth alone, nor do I expect to. I am not an engineer, nor a design technologist, so I could no more produce one of these solid-state coherent infrared insect transmitters than Goddard could have produced a Saturn rocket and gone to the moon by himself.

As more and more study and better brains than mine are put into researching the function of these elegant spine organs, then the ideas presented here will be modified and revised, just as the hydrogen model of the atom has been modified and revised over the decades. It is not important that every last word written here be correct. It is only important that I should have pointed out a new path to explore, and that, wherever that path may lead, it should stimulate more and more imaginative young biologists, chemists and physicists to look with awe upon the designs of nature. It is extremely important and necessary that capable young biologists be stimulated to study in detail that great "sea" of natural infrared radiation in which we dwell. It has been far too long a neglected sea.

What is important to my life as a scientist is not that I am right or wrong, but that whenever I gaze into the Florida sky and see a white-headed eagle suspended in the vast space of air and light, I can feel my arms around the sons and daughters of this nation, and can believe in my heart that I have tried to lead the way as best I can — or, as an anonymous poet once wrote:

> The night was dark, the road was black,
> Only an owl could see the track;
> But the cheerful driver made his way
> Through the deep pine woods as though 'twere day.
> I asked him, "How do you manage to see?
> The road and the forest seem one to me!"
> "To me as well," he did reply,
> "I can only drive by the path in the sky."
> I looked about where the treetops tall
> Rose from the ground like an ebony wall;
> And lo, a beautiful starry lane
> Wound as the road wound and made it plain.
> Thus, when our path is dark below,
> And we see not a step of the way we go,
> Then, ah then, we can gaze on high
> And walk on Earth by the path in the sky.

Glossary

Glossary

Absolute Temperature (Kelvin). The unit of measurement of absolute temperature in which absolute 0 equals -273.16° C on the centigrade scale. Named after Lord Kelvin.

Absorption. The process of taking in and transforming radiant energy into a different form, with a resulting rise in temperature (as when the Earth absorbs sunlight).

AC Generator. A generator of electric current that reverses its direction at regular recurring intervals, with each successive sine wave being equal in size and shape.

Aldehyde. Any of a class of very reactive organic compounds characterized by the group CHO (carbon-hydrogen-oxygen), and with two fewer H atoms than primary alcohols.

Alternator. (2&3 phase) another term for an AC generator.

Ampere. The practical unit of electrical current — equal to the steady current produced by one volt applied across a resistance of one ohm. An ohm is the practical unit of electrical resistance so that a potential difference of one volt produces a current of one ampere across a resistance of one ohm.

Amplification. The process of amplifying.

Amplify. To utilize an input of voltage, current, or power, so as to obtain an output of greater magnitude.

Amplitude (of radiation). The extent of a vibratory movement, or of an oscillation — the topmost and bottommost portion of a sine wave.

Angle of Incidence. The angle that a ray of light falling on a surface makes with a line perpendicular to the surface.

Angle of Reflection. The angle that a reflected ray of light makes with a line perpendicular to the surface.

Antenna. 1. A device, usually metal and constructed of rods or wire, for radiating or receiving radio waves. 2. One of the paired, movable sensory appendages of the preoral segments of the heads of insects.

Assembling. The behavioral term that Dr. H. B. D. Kettlewell, an authority on moth behavior, applies to the attraction between moths of a single species.

Aura. A distinctive highly individualized atmosphere surrounding, or attributed to, a given source, most commonly referring to a luminous radiation or enveloping glow.

Azimuth. A line of course or direction around a 360° circle.

Background Radiation. Radiation that fills the background surrounding a point source of radiation; the day sky or night sky against which one observes a visible source of radiation. There are background radiations in all regions of the spectrum, including the radio and infrared regions.

Bionics. The science of solving problems by discovering, recognizing and applying techniques that have evolved in living things to solving man's technological problems.

Biosphere. The part of the world in which life can exist.

Black Body. An ideal body or surface that completely absorbs all radiant energy of any wavelength falling upon it with no reflection of energy.

Black Body Radiation. The characteristic radiation emitted by a black body when heated.

Blacklight. A fluorescent light bulb that emits near UV radiation particularly at 0.36 micrometer wavelengths. It also emits black body infrared radiation and a small amount of visible (blue) radiation.

Bolometer. A very sensitive resistance thermometer used in the detection and measurement of weak thermal infrared radiation.

Broadband Radiation. Radiation that contains many, many narrow wavelengths such as visible light which is composed of all of the colors of the visible spectrum from violet to red. All radiations, including radio and infrared, may be broadband or narrowband. Blackbody infrared radiation is broadband.

Bursa Copulatrix. The copulatory pouch of the female of moths and butterflies that receives the male spermatophore which contains the sperm.

Chromophore. A functional (chemical) group that gives rise to color in a molecule.

Claspers. The paired retractable appendages at the tip of the male moth and butterfly. They are utilized to clasp the tip of the female abdomen during copulation.

Coherent Radiation. Waves of electromagnetic radiation in which the peaks and dips match one another in both time and space.

Collembola. An order of wingless insects. They are believed by some to represent the oldest existing group according to evolutionary theory.

Collisions (Atomic). An encounter between particles (atoms or molecules) resulting in exchange or transformation of energy.

Condensor (or Capacitator). A device giving desired values of capacitance in which opposite plates are oppositely charged by a source of voltage, and which stores the charge.

Conduction. The maintenance of an electrical current through metals (or other conductors) by a general movement of electrons along the conductor.

Conductor. A metal or other material that conducts electrical current.

Corona. A crown, or faint glow, adjacent to or surrounding a conducting object. The corona is often detected in the visible spectrum, but may occur in any portion of the electromagnetic spectrum including the infrared region.

Current. A movement of positive or negative electric particles (as electrons) accompanied by such observable effects as the production of heat, the presence of a magnetic field, or of a chemical transformation.

Density. The mass of a substance per unit volume.

Detector. A device for determining the presence of a signal after the signal is collected by an antenna.

Dielectric. An insulative substance in which a steady electric field can be set up with a negligible flow of current.

Dielectric Waveguide. A system for collecting or guiding electromagnetic waves constructed of a dielectric (insulative) substance such as wax or plexiglass. The electromagnetic energy couples directly from the source of the waves to the waveguide.

Dipole. A pair of equal and opposite electric charges (or magnetic poles) of opposite sign (+ and -) separated by a small gap.

Diptera. An order of insects characterized by having only one pair of wings.

Ecology. A branch of science that is concerned with interrelationships of organisms and their environment.

Electret. A dielectric (insulative) body in which polarization has been set up — plus on one side, minus on the other.

Electric Field. A region established by the proximity of electric charges.

Electromagnetic Radiation. A succession of (electromagnetic) waves that are propagated by simultaneous periodic variations of electric and magnetic field intensities; includes all wavelengths in the spectrum.

Emission. An act of sending forth, such as the flow of electrons from a heated filament or cathode; producing light.

Endogenous. Originating from within the body.

Energy. An entity rated as the most fundamental of all physical concepts and usually regarded as the equivalent of, or the capacity for, doing work.

Energy Level. One of the quantum states of electrons in atoms or molecules, levels of orbit of electrons around the nucleus.

Entomologist. A student of insects.

Entropy. The measure of energy's dissipation to a useless form as heat.

Epicuticle. The outermost region of the insect exoskeleton that includes the waxy layer..

Epithelium. Innermost tissue beneath an insect's hard body wall.

Equilibrium. A state of balance between or among opposing forces or processes resulting in the absence of acceleration, or the absence of net change.

Etymologist. A student of words.

Exogenous. Produced or originating from without due to external causes.

Exoskeleton. An external skeleton, the collection of sclerites covering the body of insects.

Fluorescence. The emission by a substance of electromagnetic radiation, especially visible or infrared wavelengths, as the immediate result of, and only during, the absorption of radiation from another source.

Free Electrons. An electron not permanently attached to an atom.

Frenulum. A hook-like spine on the front edge of a moth's hind wing that interlocks with a process on the front wing and unites the wings.

Frequency. The number of complete alternations (sine waves) per second of an alternating electric current or wavelength of electromagnetic radiation.

Fusion. The union of atomic nuclei to form heavier nuclei, resulting in the release of enormous quantities of energy when certain light elements unite, *i.e.*, the combination of heavy hydrogen nuclei to form helium nuclei as occurs in the sun or hydrogen bomb.

Galaxy. One of the billions of large systems of stars, including not only stars (suns), but nebulae, planets and other interstellar matter that make up the universe.

Glide Path. The path of descent of a flying object, a radio beam along which a pilot can guide his aircraft to a safe descent.

Hertz. A unit of frequency of a periodic process (sine wave) equal to one cycle per second; named after Hertz, the German discoverer of radio wavelengths.

High Energy Radiation. Radiation with high electron volt energy, generally considered as that portion of the electromagnetic spectrum of wavelengths in the UV region, and shorter. It is dangerous to organic life.

Hydrocarbon. Any of a large class of organic compounds containing only carbon and hydrogen, *e.g.*, paraffins, benzene, etc.

Impedance (Electrical). The apparent opposition in an electrical circuit to the flow of an alternating current that is analogous to the actual electrical resistance to a direct current.

Incoherent. Lacking coherence; refers to wavelengths that are out of phase in time and/or space.

Integument. The outer covering, or exoskeleton, of an insect.

Interference (Constructive). The mutual effect on meeting of two wave trains of the same type so that the waves add together to produce light lines.

Interference (Destructive). The mutual effect on meeting of two wave trains of the same type so that the waves cancel each other to produce dark lines.

Interferometer. An instrument for the precise determination of wavelengths.

Ion. An atom or group of atoms that carry a positive or negative electrical charge as a result of having lost, or gained, one or more electrons.

Johnston's Organ. A sense organ in the second antennal segment of insects that responds to movements, usually vibrations, of the antenna.

Laser (Light Amplification by Stimulated Emission of Radiation). A device that utilizes the natural oscillations of atoms for amplifying or generating electromagnetic waves in the visible region of the spectrum, common usage also covers infrared micrometer waves, but I prefer to use the term MASER for the infrared region.

Lifetime (of Radiation). The duration of the existence of an ion or subatomic particle.

Logarithm. The exponent that indicates the power to which a number must be raised to produce a given number, *e.g.*, 4 is the log of 16 to the base 2 ($2^4 = 16$).

Low-Energy Radiation. Radiation with low-electron volt energy, generally considered as that portion of the electromagnetic spectrum of wavelengths in the visible region and at longer wavelengths through the infrared and radio. It is not dangerous to organic life.

Magnetic Field. A region subject to the influence of magnetism, which is manifested by the mechanical forces that it exerts upon electricity moving across it.

Maser. See *LASER*.

Mass. The property of a body that is a measure of its inertia, commonly taken as a measure of the amount of material it contains, and that causes a body to have weight in a gravitational field.

Metastable State. An energy level state where electrons are stored before dropping back to equilibrium at ground state.

Metric System.

1 kilometer (1000 meters)	= 0.6214 miles
1 meter (100 centimeters)	= 39.37 inches
1 centimeter (10 millimeters)	= 0.3937 inches
1 millimeter (1000 micrometers)	= 0.03937 inches

Micrometer. There are 1,000 micrometers (μm) in 1 millimeter (mm).

Mitochondrion. A granular, globular or rod-like chondriosome, apparently self-perpetuating lipoprotein complexes in the cytoplasm of most cells that are thought to function in cellular metabolism and secretion.

Modulation. The variation of a characteristic (amplitude, frequency or phase) of a carrier or signal in a periodic, or intermittent manner for the transmission of intelligence.

Molecule. A unit of matter that is the smallest particle of an element, or chemical combination of atoms (as a compound) capable of retaining chemical identity with the substance in mass.

Morphology. Branch of biology that deals with the form and structure of plants and animals and the evolutionary development of biological structure.

Narrowband Radiation. Radiation of narrowband wavelength (bandwidth) and fixed frequency. Although the term narrowband is relative, colors may be thought of as having narrowband widths within the visible white light spectrum.

Nebula. Any of many immense bodies of highly rarefied gas or dust in the interstellar space of our own Milky Way and other galaxies.

Noctuid Moths. A large nearly cosmopolitan family of medium-sized, stout-bodied, dull-colored, night-flying moths. The family includes destructive agricultural pests such as the corn earworm, cutworms, and armyworms.

Nucleus (Atomic). The positively charged portion of an atom that comprises nearly all of the atomic mass.

Octave. In an electromagnetic spectrum, an interval analogous to the musical octave and being such that the frequencies at its beginning and end are to each other as 1:2. The electromagnetic spectrum from long wave radio to cosmic rays covers about 60 octaves of which visible light covers one octave.

Olfaction. The sense of smell.

Open Resonator. A resonating system for collecting or guiding electromagnetic energy in which the waves that are focused ride on the outside of the waveguide (or between mirrors separated by a space), and which is one wavelength or multiples of one wavelength, *e.g.*, dielectric waveguide or antenna.

Oscillator. A device for producing electric, electromagnetic, or audio oscillations; a sine wave frequency producer.

Osmic Frequencies. Absorption bands caused by the intermolecular vibrations of molecules.

Phase. A stage or interval in a cycle, or the periodic changes of any magnitude varying according to a simple harmonic law; in electromagnetic radiation one cycle or period being 360° or one sine wave.

Pheromone. A chemical released by a female insect that stimulates sexual attractance and response in the male. Many other pheromones are used for various types of insect communication.

Photoperiodism. The relative lengths of alternating periods of light and darkness as they affect the growth and maturity of an organism, as the flowering of plants or breeding of animals.

Phytochrome. A protein molecule found in plants, which responds to far red light and governs growth, flowering, germination and other plant life processes.

Piezoelectric. The ability of a substance to convert pressure waves to electricity. Electret substances (such as wax and teflon) have piezoelectric properties and are now used in microphones to convert sound waves into electrical current.

Plasma. An ionized gas containing about equal numbers of positive and negative ions and differing from regular gas in being a good conductor of electricity.

Prototype. The first full-scale working model of a new design of a manufactured object; primary type.

Pupa. An insect in the intermediate, usually quiescent (resting) form. It is assumed by the insects with complete metamorphosis between the larval and adult form.

Pyroelectric Detector. A detector made of a substance such as triglycine sulphate, which responds to minute temperature changes by a change in capacitance when it is radiated with infrared wavelengths.

Radio Range Station. A low-frequency (long-wavelength) radio station that sends out radio beams in four directions for guiding aircraft. Low-frequency radio range stations have now been replaced by higher frequency omniranges that send out many beams around 360°.

Radioactivity. The emission of radiant energy by radioactive substances, such as radium and uranium; usually high-electron volt energy at short wavelengths, such as beta and gamma rays. Dangerous to biological life.

Reactance (Capacitive). Electrical resistance to the flow of current that depends on the capacitance (a condenser) of the circuit.

Reactance (Inductive). Electrical resistance to the flow of current that depends on the inductance (a coil) of the circuit.

Receiver. An electrical apparatus for tuning to, and receiving, electromagnetic wavelengths — especially radio waves.

Reciprocal Law. In electronics, the law that states that anything making a good transmitting antenna also makes a good receiving antenna.

Rectifier. An electronic device for converting alternating current to direct current.

Reflection. The complete or partial return of a wave motion (light) from a surface that it encounters into the medium (air) that it originally traversed.

Refractive Index. The ratio of the velocity of light or other radiation in the first of two media to its velocity in a second as it passes from one into the other — the first media usually being a vacuum.

Relative Humidity. The ratio of absolute humidity to the maximum possible density of water vapor in the air at the same temperature. The lower the temperature, the less water vapor the air will hold in grams per cubic centimeter of air space — called absolute humidity.

Relativity. A theory formulated by Albert Einstein leading to the assertion that there is an increase in the mass of a body with an increase in velocity above the speed of light.

Replication. Repetition of an experiment or procedure at the same time and place.

Resolution. The act, process, or capability of rendering distinguishable the individual parts of an object, or closely adjacent optical images.

Resonance. The quality of being resonant; a vibration of large amplitude in a mechanical or electrical system caused by a relatively small periodic stimulus of the same or nearly the same period (sine wave), as when a radio-tuned circuit is tuned to a broadcast frequency; also the state of adjustment that produces resonance in an electrical system.

Saint Elmo's Fire. A flaming light phenomenon rarely seen in stormy weather at prominent points such as church steeples, propeller tips or tree tops. It is a free form of brush discharge of electricity causing the gases of the air to fluoresce.

Scattering. Going in different directions — as light waves being scattered by the water molecules and dust particles in the air, *i.e.,* fog.

Sclerite. The hard cuticular plates that make up the insect exoskeleton.

Sensillum, pl. Sensilla. The spine-like sense organs which are most commonly found on the antenna of insects. They may also take the form of a rod, plate, cone, cup or pit. They are dielectric waveguides, or antennae, which are used for collecting infrared radiation from resonating molecules.

Sensor. Any biological detector that responds to an environmental signal, i.e., the human eye or an insect antenna.

Side Lobes. Lobes emitted on either side of the main radiation lobe of an electromagnetic transmitter. Usually large side lobes are not desirable because they detract from the directional characteristic of a single lobe emitted from a point source of radiation such as an antenna.

Sine Wave. A fundamental waveform that represents periodic oscillations (alternating current); represented by a sine curve.

Solar Cell. A device that collects solar energy and converts it to electricity; photovoltic cell.

Spectrophotometer (Fourier Transform). A device for measuring the relative intensities (especially weak emissions) in different parts of the spectrum; used mainly in the infrared region.

Spectrum. The range of frequencies (wavelengths) of electromagnetic emissions, radio to cosmic wavelengths.

Spermatophore. A capsule or packet enclosing the sperm of insects which is inserted into the female bursa copulatrix during mating.

Substrate. The base from which an organ develops, or upon which an organism lives.

Thermoelectret. An electret that is formed by the process of melting, and then solidifying, an electret substance in an electrical field.

Time-Lapse Photography. Taking photographs at various time intervals to record growth or movement patterns.

Translucent. Admitting and diffusing light so that objects (visible) beyond cannot be clearly distinguished, partly transparent (as a fog).

Transmission. The overall proportion of radiant energy, homogeneous with respect to wavelength, that is emitted by a source of electromagnetic energy.

Transmitter. A device for transmitting radio or other electromagnetic waves.

Trichodea Sensilla. A type of long, medium or short curved sensilla found on the antenna of most species of insects. Range from 10 to 150 micrometers long.

Trichome. A hairlike structure, or spine on a plant.

Triglycinesulphate. A pyroelectric chemical (crystal) substance.

Tor. A rocky pinnacle or peak-rocky heap.

Tuned Circuit (Series). A coil and condenser in series in the antenna circuit of a receiver or transmitter to tune the antenna to an incoming wavelength.

Tuned Circuit (Parallel). A coil and condenser in parallel, and used to couple energy from one circuit (antenna or otherwise) to another circuit in a radio or transmitter.

Vector. A course or compass direction; also a line segment (quantity) having both magnitude and direction. The length of the line designates the magnitude.

Volt. The practical unit of electrical potential equal to the difference of potential between two points in a conducting wire carrying a constant current of one ampere across a resistance of one ohm.

Voltage. Electric potential or potential difference expressed in volts.

Waveguide. A metal or dielectric (insulative substance) cylinder of such dimensions that it will propagate electromagnetic waves of a given frequency.

Wavelength. The distance in the line of advance of a wave from any one point to the next point at which, at the same instant, there is the same phase; one sine wave.

Wien's Constant. The number 2,897 which, when divided by the absolute temperature (-273.16°) plus degrees centigrade, gives the peak black body wavelength of emission.

Window (Radiation). A region of the electromagnetic spectrum where the characteristic wavelengths emitted by water vapor (or other molecules) is such that they do not absorb radiation but instead allow for the transmission through the media.

Selected Readings

Selected readings

The literature covering the effects of infrared radiation on insects will be found in the references cited at the end of the author's own scientific papers. Very little research has been accomplished in this area, and other than the author's publications on the subject, there are only fourteen definitive papers by other scientists in the English language.

Abetti, Giorgio, *The History of Astronomy*. New York: Abelard-Schuman, 1952.

Acworth, Bernard, *Bird and Butterfly Mysteries*. London: Eyre and Spottiswoode, 1955.

Borgstrom, Georg, *The Hungry Planet*. London: Collier-Macmillan Ltd., 1967.

Bose, Jagadis Chandra, *Plant Response as a Means of Physiological Investigation*. New York: Longmans, Green & Co., 1906.

——, *The Nervous Mechanism of Plants*. New York: Longmans, Green & Co., 1926.

Burr, Harold Saxton, *Blueprint for Immortality*. London: Neville Spearman Ltd., 1972.

Collins, Michael and Weast, Robert D., *Wild Silk Moths of the United States*. Cedar Rapids, Iowa: Collins Radio Co., 1961.

Dethier, V. G., *The Physiology of Insect Senses*. New York: John Wiley & Sons, 1963.

Dixon, R. N., *Spectroscopy and Structure*. New York: John Wiley & Sons, 1965.

Ford, E. B., *Moths*. London: Collins, 1955.

Fraenkel, S. G., and Gunn, D. L., *The Orientation of Animals*. New York: Dover Publications, Inc., 1961.

Gates, David M., *Energy Exchange in the Biosphere*. New York: Harper & Row Biological Monographs, 1962.

Hackforth, H. L., *Infrared Radiation*. New York: McGraw-Hill Co., 1960.

Halacy, Daniel S., *Radiation, Magnetism and Living Things*. New York: Holiday House, 1966.

Hart, Ivor B., *The World of Leonardo daVinci*. New York: The Viking Press, 1961.

Haskell, P. T., *Insect Sounds*. Chicago: Quadrangle Books, Inc., 1961.

Holden, Alan, *Conductors and Semiconductors*. Bell Telephone Laboratories, Inc., 1964.

Howard, Sir Albert, *The Soil and Health*. New York: The Devin-Adair Co., 1947.

Hughes, D. O., and Latham, J. L., *Physics for Chemists and Biologists*. New York: Chemical Publishing Co., 1969.

Hulme, F. Edward, *Butterflies and Moths of the Countryside*. London: Hutchinson & Co., 1903.

Huntington, Ellsworth, *Mainsprings of Civilization*. New York: Mentor Books, 1945.

Jacobson, Martin, *Insect Sex Pheromones*. New York: Academic Press, 1972.

Kiely, D. G., *Dielectric Aerials*. New York: John Wiley & Sons, 1953.

Knight, Alice Vaile, *The Meaning of Teilhard de Chardin*. Old Greenwich, Connecticut: The Devin-Adair Co., 1974.

Krippner, Stanley and Rubin, Daniel, eds., *Galaxies of Life*. New York: Interface Book, Gordon& Breach, 1973.

Maeterlinck, Maurice, *The Life of the Ant*. New York: The John Day Co., 1930.

——, *The Life of the Bee*. New York: Mentor Books, 1954.

Marais, Eugene N., *The Soul of the White Ant*. London: Methuen & Co. Ltd., 1937.

Metcalfe, C. R. and Chalk, L., *Anatomy of the Dicotyledons*. Oxford: Clarendon Press, 1950.

Michelson, A. A., *Studies in Optics*. Chicago: The University of Chicago Press, 1962.

Moor, A. D., ed., *Electrostatics and Its Applications*. New York: John Wiley & Sons, 1973.

O'Neill, John J., *Prodigal Genius — The Life of Nikola Tesla*. New York: Ives Washburn Inc., 1944; David McKay, pb. ed., 1972.

Ott, John N., *Health and Light*. Old Greenwich, Connecticut: The

Devin-Adair Co., 1973; New York: Pocket Books, ph. ed., 1976.

———, *My Ivory Cellar*. Chicago: Twentieth Century Press, Inc., 1958; Old Greenwich, Connecticut: The Devin-Adair Co., 1973.

Pauwels, Louis and Bergier, Jacques, *The Morning of the Magicians*. New York: Avon Books, 1968.

Praeger, Robert Lloyd, *The Way That I Went*. Dublin: Allen Figgis Ltd., 1969.

———, *Natural History of Ireland*. East Ardsley, Yorkshire, England: E. P. Publishing Ltd., 1972.

Retallack, Dorothy, *The Sound of Music and Plants*. Santa Monica, California: De Vorss and Co., 1973.

Rocks, Lawrence and Runyon, Richard P., *The Energy Crisis*. New York: Crown Publishers, Inc., 1972.

Stehling, Kurt R., *Lasers and Their Applications*. New York: The World Publishing Co., 1966.

Sutton, O. G., *The Challenge of the Atmosphere*. New York: Harper & Brothers, 1961.

Tesla, Nikola, *Lectures, Patents and Articles*. Published in English by the Nikola Tesla Museum, Belgrade, Yugoslavia, 1956.

———, *Tribute to*, presented in articles, letters and documents. Published in English by the Nikola Tesla Museum, Belgrade, Yugoslavia, 1961.

Tompkins, Peter and Bird, Christopher, *The Secret Life of Plants*. New York: Harper & Row, 1973.

von Frisch, Karl, *The Dancing Bees*. New York: Harcourt, Brace & World, Inc., 1953.

Weinstein, L. A., *Open Resonators and Open Waveguides*. Boulder, Colorado: Golem Press, 1969.

Williams, C. B., *Insect Migration*. New York: The Macmillan Co., 1958.

Author's Papers

Author's Papers

Papers:

Callahan, P.S. and H. Young (1955). "Observations on the avifauna of an Ozark plateau." *Auk.* 72: 267-78.

Callahan, P.S. (1957). "Oviposition response of the corn earworm to differences in surface texture." *J. Kan. Ent. Soc.* 30:59-63.

Callahan, P.S. (1957). "Oviposition response of the imago of the corn earworm *Heliothis zea* (Boddie), to various wavelengths of light." *Ann. Entomol. Soc. Amer.* 50(5): 444-452.

Callahan, P.S. (1958). "Behavior of the imago of the corn earworm, *Heliothis zea* (Boddie), with special reference to emergence and reproduction." *Ann. Entomol. Soc. Am.* 51: 271 -283.

Callahan, P.S. (1958). "Serial morphology as a technique for determination of reproductive patterns in the corn earworm, *Heliothis zea* (Boddie)." *Ann. Entomol. Soc. Am.* 51: 413-428.

Callahan, P.S. (1958). "The strawberry sap beetle, *Lobiopa insularis.*" *Insect Conditions in Louisiana.* pp. 14- 15.

Callahan, P.S. (1958). "Survey of cutworms affecting truck crops." *Insect Conditions in Louisiana.* pp. 16-18.

Blum, M.S., J.R. Walker, and P.S. Callahan (1958). "Chemical insecticidal, and antibiotic properties of fire ant venom." *Science,* 128: 306-307.

Callahan, P.S., M.S. Blum, and J.R. Walker (1959). "Morphology and histology of the poison glands and sting of the imported fire ant (*Solenopsis saevissima v. Richter Forel*)." *Ann. Entomol. Soc. Am.* 52: 573-590.

Callahan, P.S. and J.B. Chapin (1959). "Economic moth populations in the Baton Rouge area." *Insect Conditions in Louisiana.* pp. 46-48.

Callahan, P.S., R. Brown, and A. Dearman (1960). "Control of tomato insect pests in Louisiana." *Louisiana Agriculture* 3: 1 -3.

Callahan, P.S. and J.B. Chapin (1960). "Morphology of the reproductive systems and mating in two representatives members of the family Noctuidae, *Pseudaletia unipuncta* (Haw.) and *Peridroma margaritosa* (Haw.) with comparison to *Heliothis zea* (Boddie)." *Ann. Entomol. Soc. Am.* 53: 763-782.

Callahan, P.S. and J.B. Chapin (1960). "Economic moth populations in the Baton Rouge area for 1960." *Insect Conditions in Louisiana.* pp. 46-47.

Callahan, P.S. (1961). "Relationship of the crop capacity to the depletion of the fat body and egg development in the corn earworm, *Heliothis zea,* and the fall armyworm, *Laphygma frugiperda* (Lepidoptera: Noctuidae)." *Ann. Entomol. Soc. Am.* 54: 819-827.

Callahan, P.S. (1962). "Techniques for rearing the corn earworm, *Heliothis zea* (Boddie)." *J. Econ. Entomol.* 55: 453457.

Blum, M.S. and P.S. Callahan (1963). "The venom and poison glands of

Pseudomyrmex pallidus (F. Smith)." *Phyche* 70: 70-74.

Callahan, P.S. and T. Cascio (1963). "Histology of the reproductive tracts and transmission of sperm in the corn earworm, *Heliothis zea*." *Ann. Entomol. Soc. Am.* 56: 535-556.

Callahan, P.S. (1964). "An inexpensive actinometer for continuous field recording of moonlight, daylight, or low intensity evening light." *J. Econ. Entomol.* 57: 758-760.

Callahan, P.S. (1964). "Basic semiconductor circuitry for ecological and behavioral studies of insects." *ARS* 33-94.

Callahan, P.S. (1965). "Intermediate and far infrared sensing of nocturnal insects. Part I. Evidences for a far infrared (FIR) electromagnetic theory of communication and sensing in moths and its relationship to the limiting biosphere of the corn earworm, *Heliothis zea*." *Ann. Entomol. Soc. Am.* 58: 727-745.

Callahan, P.S. (1965). "Intermediate and far infrared sensing of nocturnal insects. Part II. The compound eye of the corn earworm, *Heliothis zea*, and other moths as a mosaic optic-electromagnetic thermal radiometer." *Ann Entomol. Soc. Am.* 58: 746-756.

Callahan, P.S. (1965). "An infrared electromagnetic theory of diapause inducement and control in insects." *Ann. Entomol. Soc. Am.* 58: 561-564.

Callahan, P.S. (1965). "Far infrared emission and detection by night flying moths." *Nature*, 207: 1172-1173.

Callahan, P.S. (1965). "A photoelectric-photographic analysis of flight behavior in the corn earworm, *Heliothis zea*, and other moths." *Ann. Entomol. Soc. Am.* 58: 159-169.

Callahan, P.S. (1966). "Do insects communicate by radio?" *Animals*, 8: 197-201.

Callahan, P.S. (1966). "Electromagnetic communication in insects . . . elements of the terrestrial infrared environment, including generation, transmission, and detection by moths." *ARS* 33-110. pp. 156-176.

Callahan, P.S. (1966). "Infrared stimulation of nocturnal moths." *J. Ga. Ent. Soc.* I: 6-14.

Callahan, P.S. and A.R. Chauthani (1966). "A method for repointing insect dissecting forceps." *J. Econ. Entomol.* 59: 490-491.

Chauthani, A.R. and P.S. Callahan (1966). "A dissection technique for studying internal anatomy of different stadia of Noctuidae." *Ann. Entomol. Soc. Am.* 59: 1017-1018.

Valli, V.J. and P.S. Callahan (1966). "Biometeorological fluctuations affecting the ecology of *Heliothis zea* I." *Ga. Coastal Plain Exp. Sta. Mimeograph* Ser. N.S. 248, 11 pp.

Starks, K.J., P.S. Callahan, W.W. McMillian, and H.C. Cox (1966). "A photoelectric counter to monitor olfactory response in moths." *J. Econ. Entomol.* 59: 1015-1016.

Callahan, P.S. (1967). "Insect molecular bioelectronics: a theoretical and experimental study of insect sensillae as tubular waveguides, with particular emphasis on their dielectric and thermoelectret properties." *Misc. Public. Entomol. Soc. Amer.* 5(7): 315-347.

Snow, J.W. and P.S. Callahan (1967). "Laboratory mating studies of the corn earworm, *Heliothis zea* (Lepidoptera: Noctuidae)." *Ann. Entomol. Soc. Am.* 60: 1066-1071.

Chautharni, A.R. and P.S. Callahan (1967). "The nervous system of the corn earworrn moth, *Heliothis zea* (Lepidoptera: Noctuidae)." *Ann. Entomol. Soc. Am.* 60: 248-255.

Chauthani, A.R. and P.S. Callahan (1967). "Developmental morphology of the alimentary canal of *Heliothis zea* (Lepidoptera: Noctuidae)." *Ann. Entomol. Soc. Am.* 60: 1136-1141.

Chauthani, A.R. and P.S. Callahan (1967). "A comparison of the larval and pupal nervous systems of the corn earworm, *Heliothis zea* (Lepidoptera: Noctuidae)." *Ann. Entomol. Soc. Am.* 60:1141-1 146.

Callahan, P.S. (1968). "A high frequency dielectric waveguide on the antennae of night-flying moths (Saturnidae)." *J. Appl. Optics* 7: 1425-1430.

Callahan, P.S. (1968). "Nondestructive temperature and radiance measurements on night-flying moths." *J. Appl. Optics* 7: 1811-l817.

Manghum, C.L. and P.S. Callahan (1968). "Attraction of near-infrared radiation to *Aedes aegypti*." *J. Econ. Entomol.* 61: 36-37.

Callahan, P.S., E.F. Taschenberg, and T. Carlysle (1968). "The scape and pedicel dome sensors — a dielectric aerial waveguide on the antennae of the night-flying moths." *Ann. Entomol. Soc. Am.* 61: 934-937.

Snow, J.W. and P.S. Callahan (1968). "Biological and morphological studies of the granulate cutworrn, *Feltia subter-*

ranea (F.) in Georgia and Louisiana." *Ga. Agri. Res. Bull.* No. 42, 23 pp.

Valli, V.J. and P.S. Callahan (1968). "The effect of bioclimate on the communication system of night-flying moths." *Inter. J. Biomet.* 12: 99-118.

Callahan, P.S. (1969). Section, "infrared research," in chapter "Physical and mechanical control." *Principles of Insect Pest Management.* J.V. Osmun (ed.). *Natl. Acad. Sci.*, Wash, D.C. p. 508.

Callahan, P.S. (1970). "Evolution, ecology, and enforcement." *Assoc. Food & Drug Officials* U.S. 34(4): 227-232.

Callahan, P.S. and L. Goldman (1970). "Response of *Aedes aegypti* to 10.6 micron radiation." *First Quarterly Report*, Insect Attractants, Behavior, and Basic Biology Research Laboratory, Gainesville, Florida.

Callahan, P.S. (1971). "Far infrared stimulation of insects with the *Glagolewa-arkadiewa* 'mass radiator.'" *Fla. Entomol.* 54(2): 201-204.

Callahan, P.S. and T.C. Carlysle (1971). "A function of the epiphysis on the foreleg of the corn earworm moth, *Heliothis zea*." *Ann. Entomol. Soc. Amer.* 64(1): 309-311.

Bhatkar A., W.H., Whitcomb, W.F. Buren, P. Callahan, and T.

Carlysle (1972). "Confrontation behavior between *Lasius neoniger* (Hymenoptera: Formicidae) and the imported fire ant." *Environ. Entomol.* 1(3): 274-279.

Callahan, P.S. and T.C. Carlysle (1972). "The scanning electron microscope in agriculture research." *Sunshine State Agric. Res. Report*, Jan-Feb., 3-6.

Goldman, L.J., P.S. Callahan, and T.C. Carlysle (1972). "Tibial combs and proboscis cleaning in mosquitoes." *Ann. Entomol. Soc. Am* 65 6): 1299-1302.

Callahan, P.S., A.N. Sparks, J.W. Snow, and W.W. Copeland (1972). "Corn earworm moth: vertical distribution in nocturnal flight." *Environ. Entomol* 1: 497-503.

Callahan, P.S. and T.C. Carlysle (1972). "Comparison of the epaulette and micronodules on the tympanic membrane of the corn earworm moth with those of the cabbage looper." *Ann. Entomol. Soc. Amer.* 65(4): 918-925.

Callahan, P.S. and H.A. Denmark (1973). "Attraction of the 'lovebug' *Plecia nearctica* (Diptera: Bibionidae) to UV irradiated automobile exhaust fumes." *Fla. Entomol.* 56(2): 113-119.

Turner, W.K. and P.S. Callahan (1973). "Electrical charge on the antenna of cabbage looper, *Trichoplusia ni* (Hubner)." *First Semi-Annual Report*, Insect Attractants, Behavior, and Basic Biology Lab., Gainesville, Fla. p. 53.

Callahan, P.S. and F. Lee (1974). "A vector analysis of the infrared emission of night flying moths, with a discussion of the system as a directional homing device." *Ann. Entomol. Soc. Am.* 67: 341-355.

Callahan, P.S. (1975). "Laser in der biologie." *Laser Elektrotoptik*, Stuttgart 2: 38-39.

Callahan, P.S. (1975). "Insect antennae with special reference to the mechanism of scent detection and the evolution of the sensilla." *Int. J. Insect Physiol. & Embryol.* 4(5): 381-430.

Callahan, P.S. (1976). "The antenna of insects as an electromagnetic sensory organ." Studies on the shootborer Hypsipyla grandella (Zeller). *Misc. Public. #101*, Vol. II. J.L. Whitmore (ed). pp. 31-41.

Callahan, P.S. (1977). "Solid-state organic (pheromone-beeswax) far infrared maser." *Appl. Opt.* 16(6): 1557-1562.

Callahan, P.S. (1977). "Moth and candle: the candle flame as a sexual mimic of the coded infrared wavelengths from a moth sex scent." *Appl. Opt.* 16: 3089-3097.

Callahan, P.S. (1977). "Tapping modulation of the far infrared (17 µm region) emission from the cabbage looper pheromone (sex scent)." *Appl. Opt.* 16: 3098-3102.

Turner, W.K., P.S. Callahan, and F.L. Lee (1977). "Lack of response of cabbage looper, corn earworm and fall armyworm moths to 28, 118, and 337 µm laser radiation." *Ann. Entomol. Soc. Am.* 70(2): 234-236.

Mankin, R.W. and P.S. Callahan (1977). "Derivation of equations which relate the effective surface charge density of a dielectric or electret to measurable parameters." *J. Appl. Phys.* 48(3): 1372-1374.

Callahan, P.S. (1977). "Comments on Mark Diesendorf's critique of my review paper." *Int. J. Insect Morphol. & Embryol.* 6(2): 111-122.

Callahan, P.S. and E. Hamilton (1977). "Pumping frequency for the 17-µm ir emission from the cabbage looper moth sex scent (pheromone)." *Appl. Opt.* 16(6): 1476- 1477.

Callahan, P.S. (1977). "Tuning in to Nature." *Explorers J.* 55(4): 184-187.

Callahan, P.S. (1978). "Giant mirror of Birr." *Appl. Opt.* 17(5): 678-680.

Callahan, P.S. and R.W. Mankin (1978). "Insects as unidentified flying objects." *Appl. Opt.* 17(21): 3355-3360.

Callahan, P.S. (1979). "Insects as unidentified flying objects: author's reply to comment; 1." *Appl. Opt.* 18(16): 2724-2725.

Callahan, P.S. (1979). "Evolution of antennae, their sensilla and the mechanism of scent detection in Arthropoda." *Arthropod Phylogeny.* A.P. Gupta (ed.) Van Nostrand Reinhold Co., New York. pp. 259-298.

Callahan, P.S. (1979). "John Tyndall: unifier of 19th century science." *Appl. Opt.* 18(3): 255-258.

Callahan, P.S. (1980). 'Stimulated visible emission from insects and its relationship to nonlinear scattering of radiation and nighttime UFO sightings." *Atti della fondazione giorgio ronchi* 35: 181-190.

Callahan, P.S. (1980). "Stimulated maser-like infrared emission from water vapor doped with ammonia and insect sex attractant: biological implications." *Physiol. Chem. Phys.* 12(2): 31-38.

Mankin, R.W., K.W. Vick, M.S. Mayer, J.A. Coffelt, and P.S. Callahan (1980). "Models for dispersal of vapors in open and confined spaces: applications to sex pheromone trapping in a warehouse." *J. Chem. Ecol.* 6(5): 929-950.

Callahan, P.S. (1981). "Nonlinear IR resonance in a biological system." *Appl. Opt.* 20(22): 3827.

Callahan, P.S. (1981). "John Tyndall — contributions to the development of infrared and solid-state communications." *John Tyndall, essays on a natural philosopher.* W.H. Brock, N.D. McMillan, and R.C. Mollan (eds.). Royal Dublin Society, historical studies in Irish science and technology, no. 3. pp. 129-144.

Callahan, P.S. (1982). "Narrow band IR frequency detection by insects." *Countermeasures/counter-countermeasures Center, final report.* Dept. of the Army, Washington, DC.

Callahan, P.S., J.C. Nickerson, and W.H. Whitcomb (1982). "Attraction of ants to narrow-band (maser-like) far-infrared radiation as evidence for an insect infrared communication system." *Physiol. Chem. & Physics* 14: 139-144.

Callahan, P.S. (1983). "The possible detection of magnetic monopoles and monopole tachyons." *Spec. Sci. & Technol.* 9(1): 51-60.

Callahan, P.S. (1984). "Nonlinear maser-like radiation in biological systems." *Insect Neurochemistry and Neurophysiology.* A.B. Borkovec and T.J. Kelly (eds.) Plenum Publishing Co. pp. 337-339.

Callahan, P.S. (1985). "Picket-fence interferometer on the antenna of the Noctuidae and Pyralidae moths." *Appl. Opt.* 24(14): 2217-2220.

Callahan, P.S. (1985). "Dielectric waveguide modeling at 3.0 cm of the antenna sensilla of the lovebug, *Plecia nearctica* Hardy." *Appl. Optics,* 24: 1094-1097.

Callahan, P.S., T.C. Carlysle, and H.A. Denmark (1985). "Mechanism of attraction of the lovebug, Plecia nearctica, to southern highways: further evidence for the IR-dielectric waveguide theory of insect olfaction." *Appl. Optics,* 24: 1088-1093.

Callahan, P.S. (1988). "A possible cure for AIDS — dielectric antenna theory and virion coherence." *F.D.A. Journal*

Callahan, P.S. (1989). "Treating the AIDS virus as an antenna. 21st Century." *March-April,* 26-31.

Callahan, P.S. (1989). "Maser-like nonlinear scatter from human breath, a surface-enhanced far infrared scatter effect." *Medical Hypoth.* 28: 99-105.

Callahan, P.S. (1989). "Fourier transform studies of audio stimulated surface enhanced scatter in biological systems." *High resolution fourier transform spectroscopy 1989 technical digest series.* 6: 105-108.

Callahan, P.S. (1990). "Nonlinear infrared coherent radiation as an energy coupling mechanism in living systems." *Molecular and biological physics of living systems.* R.K. Mishra (ed.) Kluwer Academic Publishers, Netherlands. pp. 239-273.

Callahan, P.S. (1991). "Dielectric waveguide (open resonator) models of the corn earworm, sensilla: sensilla relationship to infrared coherent molecular scatter emissions from semiochemicals (Lepidoptera: Noctuidae)." *Ann. Entomol. Soc. Am.* 84(4): 361-368.

Callahan, P.S. (1993). "The mysterious round towers of Ireland: low energy radio in nature." *The Explorer's Journal,* Summer, 84-91.

Koemel, W.C. and P.S. Callahan (1994). "Relationship of extremely low frequency radio emission from flying insects to semiochemical communication." *Ann. Entomol. Soc. Am.* 87(5): 491 497.

Published Speeches:

Blum, M.S. and P.S. Callahan (1960). "Chemical and biological properties of the venom of the imported fire ant (*Solenopsis saevissima v.* Richter Forel) and the isolation of the insecticidal component." *Proc. XI Inter. Cong. Ent. Vienna, Austria.* pp. 290-293.

Callahan, P.S. (1960). "A morphological study of spermatophore placement and mating in the subfamily Plusiinae (Noctuidae: Lepidoptera)." *Proc. XI Inter. Congr. Ent. Vienna, Austria.* pp. 339-345.

Callahan, P.S. (1964). 'A photographic analysis of moth flight behavior with special reference to the theory for electromagnetic radiation as an attractive force between the sexes and to host plants." *Proc. XII Inter. Congr. Ent. London, England.* p. 302.

Callahan, P.S. (1965). "Electromagnetic communication in insects . . . determination of infrared radiance, emissivity, and temperature of arthropods." *Digest 6th Inter. Conf. Med. Electr. Biol. Engin. 34-5 Toyko, Japan.* pp. 583-584.

Callahan, P.S. (1965). "Are arthropods infrared and microwave detectors?" *Proc. N. Cen. Br. ESA* 20: 20-31.

Callahan, P.S. (1965). "Electromagnetic communication in insects . . . elements of the terrestrial infrared environment: including generation, transmission, and detection by moths." *Sci. AAAS Symposium, Montreal, Canada.*

Callahan, P.S. (1966). "Electronic instrumentation for infrared and microwave studies of insect communication systems." Proc. 19th Ann. Conf. Eng. Med. & Biol. 22: 157.

Callahan, P.S. (1967). "Electronic instrumentation for studying the insect communication system." *Proc. N. Cen. Br. ESA* 22: 28-36.

Chapin, J.B. and P.S. Callahan (1967). "A list of the Noctuidae (Lepidoptera, Insecta) collected in the vicinity of Baton Rouge, Louisiana." *Proc. La. Acad. Sc. XXX* pp. 3948.

Callahan, P.S. (1969). "The radiation environment and its relationship to possible methods of environmental control of insects." *Proc. Tall Timbers Conf. Ecol. Anim. Contr. Hab. Manag.* February 27-28, 1969. pp. 85-108.

Callahan, P.S. (1969). "Insect communication: the antenna as an electromagnetic sensory organ. Proc. Symp. on Potentials In Crop Protection." *N.Y. Agric. Exp. Stn., Geneva, N.Y.* May 20-21, 1969. pp. 3945.

Callahan, P.S. (1970). "Insects and the radiation environment." *Proc. Tall Timbers Conf. Ecol. Anim. Contr. Hab. Manag.* February 26-28, 1970. pp. 247-258.

Callahan, P.S. (1970). "Insect bioelectronics: a theoretical and experimental study of the dielectric properties of insect sensors." *Proc. Feder. Automatic Contr., Symp. Biol. Aspects Contr. Cybernetics. Yenevan, U.S.S.R.,* Vol. 1, pp. 48-63. (in Russian).

Callahan, P.S. (1970). "Sensory reception in insects." *Proc. 5th Forest Insect and Disease Contr. Conf., S.U. Forest Service, Atlanta, Ga.,* pp. 57-77.

Callahan, P.S. (1971). "Insects and the unsensed environment." *Proc. Tall Timbers Conf. Ecol. Anim. Contr. Hab. Manag.* February 25-27, 1971. pp. 85-96.

Callahan, P.S. and H.A. Denmark (1973). "The 'lovebug' phenomenon." *Proc. Tall Timbers Conf. Ecol. Anim. Contr. by Habitat Manag.* 5: 93-101.

Callahan, P.S. (1973). "Studies on the shootborer *Hypsipyla grandella* (Zellar) (Lep., Pyralidae). XIX. The antenna of insects as an electromagnetic sensory organ." *Proc. Symp. Contr. of Hypsipyla. Turrialba* 23(3): 263-274.

Callahan, P.S. (1975). "The insect antenna as a dielectric array for the detection of infrared radiation from molecules." *1st Internat. Conf. Biomed. Transducers, Paris, France.* pp. 133-138.

Callahan, P.S. (1978). "Nonlinear radiation and life — the human breath as a low intensity gasdynamic laser." *Proc. Internat. Conf. Lasers.* December 11-15, 1978. pp. 99-103.

Callahan, P.S. (1979). "Night glowing phenomenon as an indicator of insect migration routes." *Movement of Highly Mobile Insects: concepts and methodology in research.* R.L. Rabb and G.G. Kennedy (eds.) Chap. 18. pp. 257-262. *Proc. Conf. Movement of selected species of Lepidoptera in the Southeastern United States, Raleigh, NC.* Apr. 9-11, 1979.

Callahan, P.S. (1981). "Non-linear infrared radiation in biological systems with special reference to future medical applications." *Proc. 4th Inter. Conf. Human Functioning. Garvey Center, Witchita, Kansas.* September 12-14, 1980. pp. 137- 156.

Callahan, P.S. (1982). "Low energy electromagnetic radiation in relationship to body functions." *Proc. 5th Inter. Conf. Human Functioning. Garvey Center, Witchita, Kansas.* September 17-20, 1981. pp. 159-172.

Callahan, P.S. (1983). "The possible detection of magnetic monopoles and monopole tachyons." *Proc. 2nd Inter. Symp. Nonconventional Energy Technol. Atlanta, Georgia.* September 9-11, 1983. pp. 87-98.

Callahan, P.S. (1985). "New discoveries in the maser-like control frequencies of life." *Proc. 9th Inter. Conf. Human Functioning. Garvey Center, Wichita, Kansas.* September l 3- 15, 1985.

Callahan, P.S. (1988). "Maser-like nonlinear scatter from human breath — cabannes far infrared scatter effect and its relation to the AIDS virus." *Proc. Inter. Conf. Nonlinear Opt.* pp. 57-61.

Callahan, P.S. (1989). "Fourier transform studies of audio stimulated surface enhanced scatter in biological systems (insects)." *High Resolution Fourier Transform Spectroscopy, Topical Meeting. Proc. Opt. Soc. Am., Santa Fe, New Mexico.* February 13-15, 1989.

Callahan, P.S. (1990). "Solar energy — the nature of natural and 'EWEC' solar collections." *Proc 3rd Inter. New Energy Symp. Hull Quebec, Canada.* pp. 139-145.

Callahan, P.S. (1992). "Photonic ionic radio amplifier for pumping IR radiation from living systems." *Proc. Opt. Soc. Am Albuquerque, New Mexico.* Sept. 20-25, 1992.

Monographs:

'The exoskeleton of the corn earworm moth, *Heliothis zea* Lepidoptera: Noctuidae with special reference to the sensilla as polytubular dielectric arrays (1969)." *Univ. Ga. Clg. Agric. Exper. Stat. Res. Bull.* 54. 105 pp.

Callahan, P.S. (1981) "The Tilma: under infra-red radiation." *CARA studies on popular devotion*, Wash. D.C. Vol II: Guadalupan studies, No. 3. 45 pp.

Books:

Insect Behavior. (1971) Four Winds Press, New York. 155 pp.

Insects and How They Function. (1971) Holiday House, New York. 191 pp.

The Evolution of Insects. (1972) Holiday House, New York. 192 pp.

The Magnificent Birds of Prey. (1974) Holiday House, New York. 190 pp.

Bird Behavior. (1975) Four Winds Press, New York. 188 pp.

Tuning in to Nature. (1975) Devin-Adair, Old Greenwich, Conn. 240 pp. (translated into Japanese).

Birds and How They Function. (1979) Holiday House, New York. 156 pp.

The Soul of the Ghost Moth. (1981) Devin-Adair, Old Greenwich, Conn. 108 pp.

Ancient Mysteries, Modern Visions. (1984) Acres U.S.A., Metairie, Louisiana. 142 pp.

A Walk in the Sun. (1988) Acres U.S.A., Metairie, Louisiana. 241 pp.

Nature's Silent Music (1992) Acres U.S.A., Metairie, Louisiana. 224 pp.

Exploring the Spectrum (1994) Acres U.S.A., Metairie, Louisiana. 178 pp.

Paramagnetism (1995) Acres U.S.A., Metairie, Louisiana. 128 pp.

Research featured in: (partial listing)

Electronics (1965). "Bioengineering: a new discipline." 38(12): 111 -118.

Agricultural Research (1966). "Do moths use radar?"14(8): 3-4.

Time (1968). "Lifesaving light." 92(9): 48.

NASA Activities (1975). "Nature provides clues for solar energy conversion." 6(5): 9.

The Furrow (1978). "Getting along with Nature and Visionaries of 'Agri-Biology.' September-October: 4-5.

Time (1978) Pesky UFOs. l 12(21): 81.

Index

Index

AC power, 24-26
AC signal, 79-80
Adventure of Living, The, xi
aldehydes, as love bug attractants, 150-151
Ama, 100
antenna, 90-93; broadband, 158-159; comparison of insect and man-made, 96; dielectric, 92-93, 139; as dielectric collectors, 136; 91, 95-96; log-periodic, 158-159; miniature, 176; rubbing by insects, 164-165; vibrational frequencies of, 159-160, 162; 175-176
antennae, log-periodic, xii; moth, 23
array, 158
assembling, 109
atoms, explained, 133-134
attractance, system, 76
aura, infrared, 100
azimuth, 83

Bailey, Robert, 200
Berger, Robert, 139
Bergier, Jacques,203
bionics, xii, xviii, 90

biosphere, 69
Bird, Christopher, 189
black body, and pheromone emissions, 141
black body, defined, 70; infrared radiation, 78; output, 80; and pheromone emissions, 141, 198; radiation, 72, 79, 139-140;
black light, 31, 139
bolometer, 79
Bose, Jagadis Chandra, v; work with plants, 189-192
broadband, 76
bursa copulatrix, 142
Butterflies and Moths of the Countryside, 23

cabbage looper moth, 139, 156-159; pheromone testing, 162-163; pheromone signal, 172-173
cacti, 183-184, 187
candle flame, as attractant, 136; and moths, 120-123; and pheromone emission, 198
capacitive reactance, 50
Carlyle, Thomas, 23,119
Carlysle, Thelma, 114, 156, 164

Carson, Rachel, 148
chromophore, 188
circuit, tuned, 22
claspers, 143
coeloconica, 156
color spectrum, 72
colors, infrared, 64
combined atoms, 133
concentration tuning, 172
Copernicus, Nicolaus, 3
corn earworm moth, 24, 73-75, 141, 156-159, 161; sexual activities of, 142
Cronkite, Walter, 150
Crookes, Sir William, 26, 31, 126, 132-133, 136
Crown of Apulia, 121
crystal set, 91
cuticle, plant, 183

da Vinci, Leonardo, 90, 136
Dalen, Gustav, 33
Dancing Bees, The, xxi
DC signal, 79-80
de Chardin, Teilhard, xvii, xviii, 31
De Magnete, 26
Defense Department, 93, 102
Denmark, Harold, 148-149
detector, electromagnetic radiation, 90
dielectric, xiii, 107, 200; antenna, 92; efficiency of antenna, 95
dielectric rods, tapered, 94
Diptera, 61

Edison Laboratory, 24
Edison, Thomas, 34
Eguchi, Mototaro, 106
EHF (extremely high frequency), 5
electret, defined, 106-107; and environment, 108; permanence of, 107
electric control, and electrets, 108
electrical cycles, of plants, 190
Electromagnetic Bio-Information, 149

electromagnetic infrared frequencies, 90
electromagnetic radiation, 76, 135; explained, 11-13; unified theory of, 26
electromagnetic spectrum, 5, 9, 107, 134
electromagnetic waves, 202; resonating, 30
electron microscope, 101
electrons, 133
endogenous, 187
entropy, 4
epicuticle, 105; and water balance, 106
epithelium, 105
ESP, 155-156
EWEC, (Electromagnetic Wave Energy Converter), 200-202
exogenous, 187
exoskeleton, 105; of insects, 94-95
Exposition du Systeme du Monde, xxi

Fabre, J. Henri, 119, 127, 178
fall armyworms, 140
Faraday, Michael, 26
firefly, 79
flight mill, 32
flowering, photoperiodic control of, 188
fluoresce, 62-64
fluorescence, 132, 134, 165; intense, 171-172; modulated, 177
Fourier transform interferometer, 145, 159-162
Frederick II, 121, 122
frenum, 83
frequencies, 134

gases, atmospheric, 70
Gilbert, William, 26
Glagolew-Arkadiewa, Dr., 112-113
glycine, 80
Grant, G. R. M., 129
Gray, Stephen, v, 106

green wood, for fire, 198
Griffith, Paul, 176
ground state, 134
guidance system, 76

Harold, Edsel, 112
Helicoverpa zea, 24, 73
Heliothis zea, 24, 73
Henry, Joseph, 26
Herschel, William, 72, 93
Hiroshima, 9
Hook Robert, 183
hot bodies, 69, 73
Hughes, David, 36
Hulme, F. Edward, 23
humidity, and thermoelectrets, 107
Huntington, Ellsworth, 97

Indian meal moth, 145, 146
inductive reactance, 50
infrared energy, conversion to electricity, 202
infrared radiation, 5, 9; glow from, 62-64; and heat, 61-62; and insect communication, 130; and insect pits, 129
infrared signals, coded, 80-81
insect antenna, 64, 95-96; thermoelectret properties of, 114-116
insect control, through communication interruption, 174; and environmental signals, 199; by frequency system, 178
insect pheromone communication system, 174
Insects and How They Function, 78
integument, 105; and water balance, 106
interferometer, 171
IR, fluorescent energy, 135; frequency, far, 113; radiation, 70; signal as flight path, 178; signal as navigational device, 83-84; water vapor window, 159

Jander, Ursula, 164

Johnston's organ, 162-163, 178

Kant, Immanuel, 3
Kepler, Johannes, 3
Kettlewell, H. B. D., 109, 178

Laithwaite, E. R., 108, 178
Laplace, Pierre Simon, xxi
laser, 52, 110, 131-132, 172; invention of, 44-47; mirrors explained, 132-135; organic-dye, 173
lasing nature, 177-178
Le Coeur del la Matière, xvii
leaves, as open resonators, 187
log-periodic IR emission, 199
love bug, 147-150; phenomenon, 139-151
Low, F. J., 16
luminescent scents, 140

Mainsprings of Civilisation, 97
Mallach, Peter, 92
Marais, Eugene N., 128-129
maser, 110, 131-132; defined, 52; maser-like emissions, 178; frequencies, 135-136, 155, 171; radiation, 165
matter, fourth state of, 132; radiant, 132
Maxwell, James C., 26
McIndoo, N. E., 128
McKinney, Chester M., Jr., 93-94
metastable state, 134
Michelson, Albert, 44
microwave frequency, 5
microwaves, 132
modulation, 77
Morning of the Magicians, The, 203
moth, 73-85; and candle flames, 120-123; communication system, 76, 125-130; IR signals from, 82-85; life cycle, 75-76; mating experiment, 141; mating physiology, 142; noctuid, 110-111; temperature and wing vibration, 78; vision and UV, 140-141; wings of, 78

My Ivory Cellar, 89, 187

narrowband, 76
NASA (National Aeronautics and
    Space Administration), xvii, 93,
    149, 160, 200
natural radiation, 73
negative electron, 29
nettle, 183-184, 190-191
night sky, and IR emission, 142
Nobel Prize, 33, 44, 110, 112
noctuid moth, 142, antenna of,
    156; length of sensilla, 156
Noctuidae, 74

O'Neill, John, 33, 47
Okress, Ernest, 130
olfactory, insect communication,
    130
open resonator, 52, 159; antennas,
    92
Origin of Radar, The, xiv
Ott, John, 89, 187
outer cuticle, 105

Page, Robert Morris, xiv
Pauwels, Louis, 203
phase conjugation, xiv-xv
pheromones, 85; of cabbage loop-
    er moth, 139; signal distance,
    178; signal emitted, 177; signal
    manipulation, 164-165
photoperiodism, 187
Physics for Biologists and Chemists,
    33
phytochrome, 188
Pico electrometer, 189
piezoelectric, 183
pits, 129
Planck, Max, 93
plant antenna, current of, 189-190
plant hairs, 184-187
plasma, 132
Poincare, Henri, 171
polycrystalline waxes, 107
Praeger, Robert Lloyd, xx
Prodigal Genius, 29, 39
pyroelectric, 183; detector, 80

radiation, 13; background, 77;
    narrowband, 177; natural, 15
radio energy, 91
radio waves, 26, 36
reactance, 50
remote control, 31
replication, 156
resolution, 92
resonance, 43-44
resonating circuit, 26
resonators, open 159
Retallack, Dorothy, 191
reverse bionics, xviii, 90
Riley, C. V., 125, 132
RIM (Russian Infrared Machine),
    112-113

Saturna pavonia, 23
scent molecules, 64, 110, as fluo-
    rescence, 135; manipulation of,
    174; and moth attraction, 108-
    109; and radiation absorption,
    140
Science, 132
sclerites, 105
Secret Life of Plants, The, 189, 190
sensilla, xii, xvii, 23, 101, 105, 111;
    as antenna waveguide systems,
    174; 176; as dielectric wave-
    guide, 108; examples of, 98-99;
    length, 112; sensory, 106; spac-
    ing, 158
sensor, picket fence, 156
sex scents, and radiation emission,
    140
Silent Spring, 148
sine wave, defined, 43
solar cells, conversion efficiency,
    201
solar system, creation of, 3-4
Soul of the White Ant, The, 128
Sound of Music and Plants, The, 191
spermatophore, 142
sphingid moth, 78
Sphinx ligustri, 23
St. Elmo's fire, 62
St. Paul's Without The Walls, 11-
    12

Strutt, John William, 93
sun, 199; conversion of solar energy, 200-202; energy from, 4

Tesla Arc Light Company, 24
Tesla coil, 29
Tesla, Nikola, v, 16, 21-39, 43, 69
thermoelectrets, 107-108
Thomas, J. J., 33
Thomson, J. J., 26
thoracic vibration, frequency of, 78
thorax, and IR radiation, 81-82
time-lapse photography, 89
Tompkins, Peter, 189
Tournier, Paul, xi
Townes, C. H., 44, 47, 131
"Tragedy of the Night-Moth", 119-120
trichodea, 1456
trichomes, 183, 184-187
triglycinesulphate, 80
tuned circuits, 26, 37, 43-55; first, 30; parallel, 48; series, 48
Tuning in to Nature, xiv, xi

Urtica dioica, 183
USDA, 93, 136, 148-149, 187; Insect Attractant and Behavior Laboratory, 147
UV (ultraviolet) radiation, 5

vibration, and heat, 78
visible light, as moth attractant, 122
visible radiation, 5, 9
Volta, Count Allesandro, 26
von Braun, Wernher, 94
von Frisch, Karl, xxi

Warnke, Ulrich, 149, 164
water vapor windows, 69
waveguide, 48, 52, 92, 112; open resonator, 162; dielectric theory, 130-131
waves, 43; carrier, 77; coherent, 44; incoherent, 44; standing, 48
wax, electret properties, 106; in

exoskeleton, 105; 183
Westinghouse, George, 32
white light, 76
Wien, Wilhelm, 72
Wien's constant, 72
wing vibration, and signal modulation, 80
Wright, R. H., 109

X-rays, discovery of, 31-32